PASTURES NEW

Also by Fred Secombe

HOW GREEN WAS MY CURATE
A CURATE FOR ALL SEASONS
GOODBYE CURATE
HELLO, VICAR!
A COMEDY OF CLERICAL ERRORS
THE CROWNING GLORY

Pastures New

FRED SECOMBE

Illustrated by Maxine Rogers

MICHAEL JOSEPH
LONDON

MICHAEL JOSEPH LTD

Published by the Penguin Group
27 Wrights Lane, London w8 5tz
Viking Penguin Inc., 375 Hudson Street, New York, New York 10014, USA
Penguin Books Australia Ltd, Ringwood, Victoria, Australia
Penguin Books Canada Ltd, 10 Alcorn Avenue, Toronto, Ontario, Canada m4v 3b2
Penguin Books (NZ) Ltd, 182–190 Wairau Road, Auckland 10, New Zealand

Penguin Books Ltd, Registered Offices: Harmondsworth, Middlesex, England

First published 1996
Copyright © Fred Secombe 1996

1 3 5 7 9 10 8 6 4 2

Set in 11.5/15pt Monotype Sabon
Typeset by Datix International Limited, Bungay, Suffolk
Printed in England by Clays Ltd, St Ives plc

A CIP catalogue record for this book is available from the British Library

ISBN 0 7181 4147 4

The moral right of the author has been asserted

To my friend Peter Hodgens, whose
invaluable help and expertise meant
so much to me in Pastures New.

He was sitting, slouched, in his choir robes, with one arm trailed across the top of the pew. Unprepossessing in appearance, with a jutting jaw and a pair of National Health spectacles sheltering staring eyes, he had strutted his way down the aisle, in the procession, his head jerking from side to side as he examined the congregation. The occasion was my first sermon in my new parish church of Abergelly. After I had been preaching for five minutes he emitted a sigh which must have been audible at the back of the church. Then he thrust his hand inside his surplice and produced a large pocket watch to check the time. This was followed by a yawn, as loud as the sigh.

What amazed me was the way in which his antics were ignored by his fellow choristers and the congregation, all of whom concentrated their attention on me. Encouraged by such a flattering response, I continued to the end of my peroration, undeterred by the eccentric behaviour of the gentleman facing me beneath the pulpit. Unlike the church of my previous parish where the choir stalls were in the chancel and behind the preacher, in St Peter's, Abergelly, the choir filed into the pews at the front of the nave. There was a large chancel where the only furniture was provided by two ornate reading-desks. As we made our way down the aisle at the end of the service I made a mental note of the need for a change in the arrangements for the choir seating.

After the vestry prayer, one of the basses, a tall thin man with a prominent Adam's apple, came up to me and said in *sotto voce* tones, 'Apologies for the behaviour of Herbert Evans, Vicar. He's like that every Sunday. As a matter of fact, a few Sundays ago we had the Reverend Elias Williams, a retired parson who has been helping out in the interregnum. When Herbert had pulled out his watch for the third time, the Reverend Williams said, "It's eight minutes to twelve and my sermon has just three more sentences to go, Mr Evans." It raised a big laugh but the next Sunday the watch was coming out once again and the yawns were louder than ever. He has the hide of a rhinoceros but the memory of an elephant. He knows the number of almost all the hymns in Ancient and Modern, even the ones that are never sung. By the way, my name is Ivor Hodges and I am headmaster of the local Secondary Modern school. You must come and see us once you are settled down. We'd be pleased to see you.'

That was the beginning of a long friendship which helped to ease my way into my new environment. I was only thirty-four years of age and needed all the support I could get to cope with the task of ministering to a huge parish where the previous incumbent had been in charge for more than thirty years. Post-war development had created a big housing estate perched on the hill overlooking the town. A church had to be built to accommodate a community devoid of any social centre. This was a problem, too, for my wife, Eleanor, a doctor, who was endeavouring to set up a practice to serve the benighted population. A further complication was the necessity to give some priority to our young family – David who was four and our one-year-old daughter, Elspeth. When the Bishop had offered me the living I had felt honoured to be given such promotion. Now the euphoria was fading and a grim assessment of the task confronting me had taken its place.

The following evening I held my first Parochial Church Council meeting in the church hall, a red-brick building erected at the turn of the century. It was situated in a busy street, some distance away from the parish church. Signs of neglect were everywhere. Many years had passed since any paint had been applied to the woodwork and the walls. Damp had begun to make inroads into the ceiling and some of the walls where the plaster had parted company with the bricks in unsightly patches. It was becoming obvious to me that, before I tackled the problem presented by the housing estate, I would have to raise the morale of the parish church congregation by renovating the church hall and redecorating the interior of the church.

Twenty chairs had been put out in the musty-smelling classroom set aside for the meeting. They were cheap tubular constructions, easy to stack and uncomfortable to sit on. Behind a table at the front were four wooden chairs which had survived the ravages of time and woodworm. These were to accommodate the two churchwardens, the secretary and the Vicar. I had arrived early and was met by Sid Thomas, a plump little man who was the secretary. He was an accounts clerk at the colliery, and in his time had played as scrum-half for Abergelly when the club was in its halcyon days. Now his beer drinking had expanded his waistline to such an extent that he would have been unable to see a rugby ball if it was at his feet.

The Church Scouts were holding some kind of jamboree in the main hall and the noise was deafening.

'I've told them already about the din, Vicar, but I may as well talk to the wall. Willie James has got no control of them at all. He's as daft as a brush with them. They walk all over him. He hasn't turned up yet, as usual. Not that it will make much difference when he does come. Perhaps you could have a word with them, Vicar. They might listen to you, if you ask them to keep the noise down.'

I went out into the mayhem immediately and was struck on the back of the head by a football propelled at a speed worthy of an international centre-forward. There was an instant silence. I turned round to find the culprit, a burly teenager whose frame was bursting out of the Scout uniform in which it was incarcerated. His face a deep crimson caused by a mixture of embarrassment and physical exertion, he looked at the floor in the vain hope that it would remove him from the scene. Then, addressing the floor, he murmured, 'Sorry, sir, I wasn't expecting you to come out of the classroom.'

'I'm sure you weren't,' I replied. 'A church hall is not a football field. I tell you now, if you persist in treating it as if it were, you will have to go elsewhere for your activities. In a quarter of an hour's time, I shall be holding a meeting in the classroom. If you make as much noise as you have been doing since I have been here, I shall come out and ask your Scoutmaster to take you from here and into the nearest park.'

No sooner had I finished speaking than the door at the back of the hall opened and the Scoutmaster appeared. A diminutive figure whose short trousers were covering his kneecaps, he peered at me through his rimless spectacles. 'Ah! Good evening, Vicar,' he boomed in a deep bass voice more suited to a six-foot presence than one of barely five foot. He advanced towards me with his hand outstretched. 'We meet, at last.' Since I had been in the parish for only three days, I felt his remark should have been reserved for a 'Doctor Livingstone, I presume' occasion.

As we shook hands, I said, 'Your Scouts have been more than a little boisterous. We are about to hold a Parochial Church Council meeting in one of the classrooms. I have told them that, unless they calm down, they will have to take themselves and their football to the nearest park.'

'Don't worry, Vicar,' he replied. 'I shall take them out there in any case. We don't want to cause you any inconvenience. Right, boys. Let's make our way to the park.' It was the signal for a stampede towards the door. There was a collision with members of the PCC who were making their way to the meeting. Leading the contingent was Amos Perkins MPS, Abergelly's answer to Boots the Chemist and Vicar's Warden. He was a large red-faced man whose upper lip sported a greying Hitler moustache. He peered at the exuberant Scout troop through his expensive tortoiseshell spectacles.

'How many times have I told you boys to behave yourselves instead of acting like hooligans,' he shouted. It was more of a bray than a shout. At that instant I decided I would dispense with his services at the next Easter Vestry meeting on the principle that no parish could serve two masters.

'I have already had words with them, Mr Perkins,' I said quietly. 'I think it was a case of over-enthusiasm, rather than hooliganism. I'm sure that you were a boy once.'

He glowered at me. 'When I was a boy, I had more respect

for my elders than they have,' he snorted. It was not an auspicious prelude to the meeting.

Ten minutes later every seat was taken for the first Parochial Church Council gathering under the new regime. On my right hand at the table was Tom Beynon, People's Warden, a short stocky bald-headed man whose head and face were decorated with blue scars, the miner's trademark. With an open countenance and ever-present twinkle in his eye, he had been the people's choice for twenty years. His only vice was his devotion to an evil-smelling pipe whose fumes had heralded his entry into the church hall. My call to prayer to open the meeting was followed by the abandonment of his comforter, which lay on the table in front of him, still reeking but dormant at least for the duration of the meeting. The minutes were read by Sid Thomas at great speed. He seemed anxious to bury the past as quickly as possible to get on with the agenda of the future. Later on I discovered that he always read that fast, either through nervousness or perhaps because no one would be able to question the veracity of his record. The minutes were passed and no one wished to raise any matter arising from them.

There was an expectant hush as I began my inaugural address. 'It is no easy task for someone of my age to follow in the footsteps of a priest who has ministered in this parish for more than thirty years and whose name is respected throughout the diocese.' (Hear! Hear!) 'However, this is the challenge the Bishop has given me and with God's help and your cooperation I shall try to face it.' (Hear! Hear!) 'That is not the only challenge. There is a church to be built to serve those who are stranded on that big new housing estate. Then there is the state of this church hall, badly in need of renova-

6

tion, not to mention the lack of decoration in the church itself.' By now the initial enthusiasm showed signs of diminution amongst some of the members. My next few words caused a considerable drop in the temperature. 'I have been looking through the registers and I was appalled to find that in a parish of this importance the average weekly giving is in the region of fourteen pounds and ten shillings from congregations which amount to well nigh two hundred per Sunday. This is an insult to the Almighty whom they come to worship. There is no unemployment in this flourishing town. If we are to work together to make a worthy response to these challenges, we must begin by putting our hands deeper into our pockets. That is priority number one.' The expectant hush had given way to a sullen silence.

Undaunted I continued with the list of priorities. 'Number two is a commitment to give some of our time to help with the renovation and redecoration of this church hall and in the church itself. In my last parish, to celebrate its centenary the church was completely and beautifully redecorated by voluntary labour. I am sure that the same can be achieved here in Abergelly. Number three is a further commitment to reach out to the non-church going element in this town by doing a door-to-door visitation, especially on the housing estate to discover the nominal Anglicans, if one may use that term to describe those who were baptised, perhaps confirmed, in the Church in Wales. Number four is to give the Holy Communion its rightful place in our worship by making it the main service on a Sunday instead of relegating it to a said service at eight o'clock in the morning attended by a handful of worshippers. Once I have prepared the way by preaching a series of sermons on the Eucharist at the eleven o'clock Matins, we shall make our main service a Sunday Family Communion at nine-thirty or ten a.m. every Sunday. I am sorry to have bludgeoned you so brutally at this first meeting but I felt it right to let you know of my intentions now. The task confronting us is a very big one and calls for candour from the outset. I have had my say and now I shall be very pleased to hear what you think about it.'

I sat down, glad to rest my legs which were now weak at the knees as I began to realise the extent of my temerity. There must have been at least a minute's silence before the first speaker was on his feet. As I half expected, it was the burly figure of Amos Perkins alongside me.

Ignoring me and addressing the members of the PCC directly, he said, breathing heavily, 'Well, I don't know what you all thought of that. All I can say is this is the first I have heard about all these priorities. As Vicar's Warden, I should have been told of what he had in mind. He talks about an insult to the Almighty. He says nothing about insulting us with his remarks about our giving and the state of the church hall and so on. Then he goes on to tell us that the services which have been part of our worship for generations are all going to be changed. What kind of people do you think we are? The Vicar was respected everywhere in the diocese, you began by telling us. Are you saying that he has left this parish in a mess after giving thirty years of his life to it.' The longer he persisted in his harangue the more obvious it was from his listeners' faces that he was losing the support he thought that he would gain. His voice had an unpleasant edge to it and was beginning to grate on the ears as his expostulations grew in intensity. 'Let me tell you this. If you think you are going to get support for your big ideas, you are going the wrong way about it.'

As he resumed his seat, he looked around at his audience, as if expecting a round of applause. Apart from a few half-hearted handclaps, there was nothing. Then, to my great relief, Tom Beynon stood up. I felt that if anybody could pour oil on the troubled waters, it would be he.

'Well, Vicar,' he began, giving me my title, which his fellow warden had used for my predecessor. 'I am sorry that Mr Perkins has spoken like he has. He complains that he should have been told about what you had in mind for us in Abergelly. You haven't told me anything either. I didn't expect you to. All I know is that I came here tonight to listen to what you had to say. To be honest I must say that I was a bit put out, as every one of us was. Anyway, as it sinks in, I'm sure that you have every right to put the facts before us. Yes, we haven't been giving what we should. Yes, this church hall is a disgrace. Above all, yes, we have got to do something for those people up on the Brynfelin estate. You are a young man, Vicar. You have got the energy and the enthusiasm. All I hope is that we will have enough puff in us to follow you up this mountain you have given us to climb. I'll do my best and I hope all of us will.' He turned to me and shook my hand. It was the most welcome handshake I have ever had. There was some desultory applause, at least more than there was for the Perkins diatribe. I waited for further contributions to the discussion. A number of hands went up.

I pointed to a man who was sitting in the front row opposite me. He was one of the few who had clapped Amos Perkins. In the interests of fair play and in the hope that he would be as crass as the Vicar's Warden, I waited for his words. He stood up belligerently and looked around at his listeners, like Amos.

''Ow on earth do you think that we can carry out these four wot-you-calls you have been talking about? I 'ave 'ad the job of keeping a list of the money in the envelopes every Sunday. I know all of those people, not like you, and I can tell you that is all they can afford out of their weekly wot-you-call. This is Abergelly not Newport or Cardiff. We're all working-class 'ere and not like those wot-you-call classes with their posh 'ouses and cars. That's all I've got to say.'

Tom Beynon nudged me and whispered in my ear, 'That's "Wot-you-Call" Williams.' My confidence was beginning to grow. If Wot-you-Call Williams was typical of the Amos Perkins band of supporters, I had nothing to fear.

One by one various members of the PCC expressed their opinions, most of them pro the priorities as they had time to reflect on them. Last of all, a hand was raised at the back of the meeting. As the speaker stood, I recognised him as Ivor Hodges, the chorister and headmaster who had apologised for Herbert Evans' behaviour.

'I have listened intently to all that has been said this evening,' he said. 'It seems to me that our new Vicar is someone sent to us by the Almighty. Anything which has been said to decry his blueprint for our parish's future has been the product of a reluctance to face the facts and a desire to let things drift because anything else would involve self-sacrifice. I urge you to give this man the vote of confidence which he deserves. I propose that this meeting supports all the propositions he has outlined.'

'I second that,' announced one of the few ladies present.

'As someone who has seen this parish close its eyes to its obligations for far too long.'

'All those in favour of the proposition, will you please raise your hands?' I asked.

After half-a-dozen hands were raised initially, another ten joined them eventually, leaving eight hands to signify their opposition. It was a result far in excess of my expectations when Amos Perkins had risen to his feet to launch such a vituperative attack upon me.

Before I said the grace to end the meeting, I said, 'I must thank you all for the confidence you have shown in me. My one hope is that it can be justified in the years that lie ahead. It is only by God's help that this can be realised. Let us pray.'

Such a deep silence followed that I felt the Lord had answered my prayer.

As the meeting broke up, I turned towards Amos Perkins only to find that he had gone to shake hands with Wot-you-Call Williams. A few malcontents joined this nucleus of dis-union. In the meanwhile I was surrounded by a cordon of well-wishers assuring me of their support.

'I suppose, at the next meeting, we must select an action committee to get things under way, I said. 'Thank you, Tom, for what you have done this evening. You represent the people and without your lead my words would have fallen on deaf ears. My only sorrow is that the vote was not unanimous.'

'It's only in fairy tales that everybody's happy,' he replied. 'Look, Vicar, in every parish there's always somebody who's like that dog-in-the-manger. I'm sure that those horses and cows took no notice of him. They'd heard him bark before and much good it did him and that's how it is here.'

When I went back to the Vicarage, my wife greeted me with an embrace.

'Well, my sweet,' she enquired, 'and how did it go? Not that I have any need to ask. I can tell by your face that all was well.'

I kissed her. 'Not exactly,' I replied. 'Sixteen for and eight against. Two thirds majority.'

'The Prime Minister would love that,' she said.

'Believe it or not,' I added, 'the eight against were led by my own warden.'

'I can fully believe that,' she asserted very forcefully. 'As soon as I met that man with his Hitler moustache and his strutting manner I knew he would be your arch enemy in everything you attempted to do in Abergelly. All he needs is a brown shirt and swastika armband – at least you know where to look for the source of any anti-Secombe trouble in the parish. There will be no possibility of a knife in the back from the unknown.

'My worry is that I can't find out who is behind the opposition to the granting of a council house for use as a surgery from the housing Committee. Why they keep putting it off, I don't understand. The need is urgent, as you well know.'

'Perhaps there is no sinister intent,' I said. 'It may simply be another example of the creaking machinery of local government in this part of the world. Some pettifogging official exerting his authority.'

'I tell you what,' she replied. 'If I don't hear anything within the next few days, I shall write a letter to the *South Wales Argus*.'

A week later a young man appeared on our doorstep announcing that he was from the *Argus* and wishing to speak to my wife. 'We have had a letter from her complaining about the inaction of the Council Housing Committee in granting her the use of a Council house as a surgery. The Council's neglect of the new Brynfelin housing estate is becoming the talk of the valley. This is just one more instance of it.'

Eleanor was upstairs bathing our daughter. It was Marlene's day off. Our nursemaid went home to Pontywen every Tuesday to visit her mother. I ushered the reporter into the sitting-room and sped upstairs. My wife was seated on the closed toilet lid, drying Elspeth in a bath towel large enough to cover both my son and my daughter.

'Where's the fire?' she demanded.

'Downstairs,' I gasped, 'and, believe me, it's a big one.'

She looked at me in alarm. 'What do you mean?' she asked.

'The *South Wales Argus* have sent a reporter after receiving your letter, and they want an interview with you to splash on the front page.'

'Dry her,' commanded my wife. 'I'll have to go into our bedroom and tidy myself up. Why in God's name did he have to come this early?' Before I could attempt a reply she had disappeared. Elspeth looked up at me with wondering eyes. It was the first time that I had been responsible for her bathroom welfare.

'Mummy will be back soon. Daddy will dry you.' I cuddled her rather than dried her. She snuggled into me and I took Eleanor's place on the toilet lid, leaning against the water tank as if it were a bedrest. As my eyelids began to close in a blissful state, I was brought back to earth by a loud instruction from my wife as she made her way downstairs.

' "Dry her," I said, not "put her back to sleep." Her clothes are set out on her bed.'

I roused myself and began to rub her gently with the

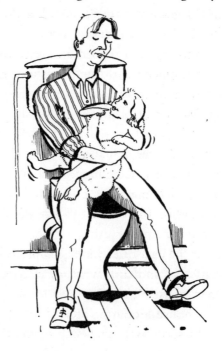

towel. Then I picked her up and carried her into her bedroom. By the time I had dressed her, I looked at my watch to discover it was twenty-five past ten. I was due to be administering the sacrament of Holy Communion to a bedridden person at half past ten. Hoisting her over my shoulder, I made my way downstairs and tapped on the sitting-room door. The conversation inside continued. I tapped again and then opened the door.

'I'm sorry to interrupt the proceedings,' I said, 'but I am afraid I shall have to leave Elspeth with you, my dear. I am due to take a sick Communion in five minutes' time.'

'The pressures of the clerical life,' commented the young man.

'Wait until I get my surgery,' added my wife. 'The pressures of a general practice are far greater.'

'Can't stop to argue,' I replied and went into my study. A minute later I rejoined the sitting-room session.

'Have you seen my stole, love?' I enquired.

'It's where you left it, dear, slung over a hook in the hall,' she replied in tones of heavy sarcasm. 'What about the pressures on a clerical wife?'

It was my first sick Communion in my new parish. My predecessor had left me a list of parishioners who had the sacrament monthly. Top of the list was the Reverend Ernest Wilkinson, a retired priest. Alongside his name was written 'Bedridden for the past three years. Former Vicar in Bath and Wells'. There were so many Welsh priests in that diocese in the past that it used to be known as Bath and Wales. I arrived at his house a quarter of an hour later, expecting a reprimand. As soon as I reached his bedside that's what I received.

'Black mark, young man,' he breathed, as his wife introduced me. She was a frail old lady whom I had met at the early morning Communion the previous Sunday. 'Salt of the earth,' Tom Beynon had whispered to me as she came through the church door after the service. She was a tiny birdlike figure, her back bent by arthritis. Her husband was sitting up, his back cushioned by pillows. It was obvious that his lungs were fighting a losing battle. Every breath was an effort. His grey face was drawn, with lines biting deep into his countenance. Under his bushy eyebrows his hooded eyes pierced into my very soul. I felt distinctly uncomfortable.

'My apologies, father,' I said meekly. 'I'm afraid we had an unexpected visitor and that caused chaos in our household. I promise that I will not transgress next time. Furthermore, if you wish, I am fully prepared to administer the sacrament weekly and on a Sunday, directly after service.' His expression softened and a slow smile transformed his appearance.

'That is very kind of you, Vicar, and much appreciated.' It was a sentence punctuated by several breaths.

'Enough talking, my dear,' said his wife. 'If you don't mind, Vicar, I shall take his part in the service as well as mine. I'm sure our Lord will understand.'

'I'm sure he will,' I replied.

When I had robed and prepared the chalice and paten on the immaculately white cloth covering the table at the bedside, I discovered a new depth in the rite according to the Book of Common Prayer. It was an unforgettable experience. 'Where two or three are gathered together in my name, there am I in the midst of them.' When the service was over nothing was said until I had cleansed the vessels and disrobed.

'Thank you,' said the Reverend Ernest Wilkinson. They were the last words I heard him speak. He died a few days later.

On my return to the Vicarage, the reporter had gone, leaving my wife excited at the prospect of front-page publicity in the local evening newspaper. 'If that will not shame them into action, nothing will,' she exclaimed.

'Have you thought that it might have the opposite effect,' I suggested. 'The ruling clique could all gang up together and invent reasons for their inaction. The last thing they will want to do is to climb down.'

'My dear love,' she replied, 'the last thing they will want to do is to lose votes at the next election and where people's health is concerned that is a number one priority. We'll see.'

The next evening's edition of the *South Wales Argus* proclaimed 'DOCTOR CONDEMNS LOCAL COUNCIL'. There followed a full account of the interview with Eleanor, with a footnote 'see Letters to the Editor on page 7'. In the letter she said that when she first approached the Council about the use of a council house as a surgery, three months before our move to Abergelly, the response was positive and encouraging. Since then she had written and phoned on a number of occasions, only to be fobbed off with excuses for their inaction. 'In the meanwhile,' she wrote, 'hundreds of families are without medical care.'

'What's the betting that you will have a phone call from the Chairman of the housing committee before the night is out,' I said to her after reading the article.

No sooner had I made that comment than the phone rang. 'What did I tell you?' I crowed. She went into my study to answer the call and closed the door behind her. It was a quarter of an hour before she emerged, with the light of triumph in her eyes.

'Secombe, you were dead right, it was the Chairman. But as a prophet, judged by your words last night, you are dead wrong. David Harris apologised at length for the delay in letting me have a surgery. He claimed that he knew nothing about it and put all the blame on his minions in the department. Had he known he would have done something about it long ago. If there is any slip up next time I must phone him immediately. He is arranging to have one of the officials to come and see me tomorrow. Well, my love, we have both got through stage one in our Abergelly campaign.' She threw her arms around me and gave me a bear hug.

'Well done, that girl,' I said. 'Without wishing to put a dampener on things, I have an uneasy feeling that all our biggest headaches are yet to come, but let's celebrate the end of stage one.'

'Remember, love,' she replied, 'your predecessor warned us that we were both facing a stern challenge. It's only just beginning. There's still one bottle left of that crate of champagne your brother sent us to apologise for his absence at your induction. "*Carpe diem*", as they say.'

2

'I have been telling my cousin about the urgent need for a church of some kind on the new Brynfelin housing estate,' said Mrs Agnes Wilkinson to me. We were in the parlour of their modest retirement house, after the funeral of her late husband, eating delicately cut sandwiches, washed down with a vintage sherry. It had been a quiet ceremony where the mourners were confined to the family and a few friends in accord with the wishes of the deceased. Throughout the service in the church and at the graveside the widow had borne herself with an impressive dignity. Now at the wake, she had assumed the role of hostess seeing that everyone was supplied with food and drink and making any introductions which were required. One of these was to play an important part in the missionary activity necessary to supply the needs of the unchurched population of the Brynfelin housing estate.

'This is my cousin Bernard Featherstone, and this is our Vicar, the Reverend Fred Secombe.' We shook hands and then our hostess added the information about the urgency of the situation at the outpost of the parish.

'You must enlarge on what my cousin has told me,' he said.

He was a tall, well-dressed man in a charcoal grey suit, bespoke, not like my Montague Burton outfit. A neatly trimmed grey moustache adorned his upper lip to complement his immaculately brushed steel-grey hair. His accent was that of an Oxbridge man with a faint trace of South Wales somewhere in the background. After I had provided a lengthy account of the problems I had inherited from my predecessor, he pursed his lips and whistled his sympathy for my predicament.

'That's some list of headaches. This church on the housing estate which is needed so badly. With the financial situation of your parish in such a poor state you can't possibly construct a permanent building for many years. By that time you will have a generation of heathens with no desire to enter it. What you want is something to accommodate a congregation now – a temporary shelter. I think I can help you with that.' My heart skipped a few beats. He smiled and said. 'Don't look so amazed, Vicar. I am the managing director of a small steelworks outside Cardiff. Recently we have had an extension built, in the course of which we had to use a wooden structure which served as offices for the firm. Now that everyone is back in the main building, it is lying idle, ready to be dismantled. I am sure that, once all the partitions inside were removed, you would have enough space to minister to a congregation of up to two hundred or so. You can have it for nothing and I shall even pay for the cost of its removal to the new site. Then it will be up to you to convert it into a place of worship. What do you say?'

'I say, thank you very much indeed, Mr Featherstone. It is extremely generous of you. First, I shall have to get the permission of the Council to erect it. As soon as that is done, we can go ahead. I am sure that there must be men in the congregation with the skills to transform it. I shall call a meeting of all those interested next week to find out what talents are available. In my last parish, parishioners themselves made a splendid job of redecorating the church. Why can't Abergelly rise to the occasion?' We shook hands warmly once again. He gave me his telephone number and home address. After he had left, I thanked Mrs Wilkinson for her help.

'My dear Vicar,' she replied, 'I know only too well the trials and tribulations of a parish priest. It seems to me that you are going to have more than your fair share of them. I'll let you into a little secret. My husband said after you had gone last week, "That young man is going to go far." Anything I can do to help you in your progress I shall be only too pleased to do it.' I kissed her on the cheek. 'Thank you for that,' she said quietly. 'It has been a trying day and I must say you have been a great support.'

It was the first time that I had come away from a funeral with a feeling of euphoria. I could not wait to get back to the Vicarage with my good news.

'You look as if you have come from a wedding not a funeral,' my wife commented as I burst in upon her in the kitchen. I waltzed her around the room. 'You are drunk,' she said.

'Smell my breath.' I replied. 'A slight trace of alcohol. No more than that.'

'All right, come out with it. What has happened?'

'We are going to have a church on the Brynfelin estate very soon.'

'Now I *know* that you are drunk,' she said scathingly.

'As St Peter said on the first Whit Sunday,' I replied: 'I am not drunk but I have gone through a great experience.'

'I never knew he said that,' Eleanor retorted.

'He didn't exactly say that but it sums up what he must have felt. It is true, love. We are going to have a church on Brynfelin. Once I have permission from the council it will be on its way within a week.'

'In that case, Frederick,' she said, 'it must be a circus tent or something similar. No way can you transport a church.'

As soon as she heard my explanation, she was equally elated. 'That's wonderful,' she exclaimed. 'A church for nothing and I am having my surgery for nothing. Well, not exactly that, I shall have to pay the rent and pay for its conversion into a surgery.'

'The same thing applies to the new church,' I replied. 'Either we get voluntary labour to turn an office block into a new church or we shall have to pay for it to be done professionally. You have the money to pay for your new surgery. The cupboard is bare in St Peter's.'

'If St Mary's Pontywen could do that renovation by voluntary labour, so can Abergelly,' she said. 'I've got a feeling that it is going to give new heart to the congregation. It means an end to the feeling of "as it was in the beginning so will it be for ever." You talked about the first Whit Sunday. This parish is going to experience its own Pentecost. I feel it in my bones.'

'I hope and pray that you are right,' I said fervently.

Later that evening I called at Tom Beynon's house to pass on the good news and to ask his opinion of the availability of voluntary labour. Winnie, his wife, opened the door to me apologising for the fact that she was still wearing her pinafore. She was a pleasant lady, with a ready smile. Unlike her husband, she was somewhat shy and not given to many words.

'I'm afraid Tom is not in at this moment but come on in, all the same. He's gone down to the off-licence to get some bottles of stout. He has a glass of stout every night before going to bed. He says it makes him sleep. That's his excuse, anyway.'

As I sat down in the front room, I found conversation very difficult. It was with great relief that I heard the key turn in the front door. He poked his head round the open door to check on the identity of the visitor. The parlour was only used to receive guests.

'Vicar,' he said warmly. 'How nice to see you. Let's go into the middle room, it's more comfortable there. I've just been down to get my nightcap. Perhaps you'll join me.'

'With pleasure,' I replied. 'All the more so because I've got some good news to let you have. So it will be more of a celebration than a nightcap.'

Winnie led the way and disappeared into the scullery, glad to be relieved of the burden of conversation.

'You can have the honour of sitting in my rocking chair,' he announced. His wife came in with two glasses. 'Tom, I'll leave the two of you to talk in peace while I go to do the ironing,' she said and went back to the scullery, closing the door behind her.

'Well, what's this good news?' he asked as he poured the dark liquid into a pint glass.

'I think you had better sit down in case the shock will be too much for you,' I answered. He raised his eyebrows as he handed me my drink. He poured out his own glassful and sat down opposite me in a large armchair. 'Here's to the new church at Brynfelin,' I said.

'What new church?' he asked, bewildered.

'Tom, we have been offered a temporary building free of charge. The one condition is that we erect it, either with voluntary labour, or professionally. I was at Mrs Wilkinson's after the funeral this afternoon and she introduced me to her cousin who is managing director of a steelworks somewhere outside Cardiff. He has offered a wooden building which used to house offices for his staff and which is now redundant. He says that once the partitions are removed from inside, it would be big enough to hold a congregation of about two hundred. He has even offered to pay for the cost of transportation to Abergelly.' I sat back and waited for his reaction.

'Vicar!' he exclaimed. 'Marvellous! Of course, we can do it with voluntary labour. I can think of several craftsmen in the congregation. Jack Richards, who's got the fish and chip shop in Monmouth Street, used to be a builder before he started up his shop. He's always willing to help and I bet he'd like the chance of being the gaffer. Bill Latham is a carpenter who works for the Council. Arnold Templeman is a retired painter and decorator and is still a fit man, despite his age. Now let's see who else we've got. Of course, there's Dai Elbow.'

'Who on earth's Dai Elbow?' I asked.

'He was the dirtiest forward who ever played for Abergelly. He put more men out with his elbow than Joe Louis did with his fists. Ended up with a lifelong ban. Anyway, he's a re-formed character these days and even comes to church with his missus at Christmas. Dai is an electrician at the colliery.'

By the time we had finished the beer, he had thought of a plumber, a bricklayer and of somebody who could supply us with a concrete mixer. 'All we need to do now, Tom, is to get permission from the Council to put up a temporary building.

I should think there should be no trouble there. I expect we shall have a lot more headaches when we apply for planning consent for a permanent construction. Do you think I should wait for a PCC meeting before I contact the Council?'

'The sooner we get cracking the better,' he replied. 'We may as well sound them out now and then put in an application after we've had a special PCC meeting. If they are going to object, then there won't be much point in having the meeting. I'm sure they won't, anyway.'

Emboldened by Tom's prognostication, next morning I rang Jeff Taylor, the official who had been in touch with Eleanor about the surgery on the estate. He had been extremely cooperative. I hoped I would receive the same treatment. He was not very reassuring.

'As far as I am concerned,' he said, 'I could tolerate it as a temporary measure. The trouble is in that word "temporary". There are many such buildings in this part of the world well over fifty years old since they were erected and they are now eyesores. Still it is not up to me personally. The decision will be made by the Planning Committee. They will ask my opinion, of course. I should have to say that the one condition I would stipulate is that it has a life of ten years only. If it has not been replaced by a permanent building by then, the building would have to be dismantled. I should think the Committee would accept your application with that proviso. I am sorry that I can't say more than that Vicar. Please give my kind regards to Dr Secombe.'

I went into the kitchen where Eleanor was peeling potatoes. Before I could pass on my news she said, 'Fred, we must get someone in to help with the cooking and the housework. Next week I shall be up on the estate and I can't see you with an apron and certainly not with a chef's hat on your head. I should have put in an advert for a daily in addition to the one I put in for a receptionist. By the way, the three applicants for that job are due here in half an hour. So I should make yourself scarce. Marlene has taken the children out. That only leaves you.'

'Before I make myself scarce, as you put it so delicately, might I be allowed to tell you what has happened about applying for the erection of our prefabricated place of worship.'

'Come on then, spit it out, Frederick,' she urged.

'Mr Jeff Taylor, who gave you his full cooperation, was not quite so forthcoming with me,' I said. 'He doesn't like temporary buildings and is going to suggest to the Planning Committee that permission to build is given only on condition that it is dismantled if there is no permanent church there in ten years' time.'

'What's wrong with that?' she replied. 'It will give the Parochial Church Council every incentive to build something worthwhile in ten years' time instead of sitting back on their posteriors and letting time drift by.'

I raised my eyes to heaven. 'But where is the money going to come from?' I demanded.

'That is up to you and the Holy Spirit,' she retorted. 'It was only last night that we were talking about another Pentecost.'

Prompted by this remark, I spent some ten minutes on my knees before the service. A few elderly ladies made their way into the church chattering loudly. 'Quiet, Mabel,' said one of them. 'The Vicar is praying in the Chancel.' The conversation disintegrated into whispers. As I rose from my prayers I wondered how the money to build a new church could be raised by a congregation which included so many pensioners. After all, the outpouring of the spirit came down upon a band of fishermen who were young and middle-aged, not upon those who were in their dotage. There were eleven communicants, ten old ladies and Llew Phillips, a retired postman who acted as a sidesman, giving out and collecting prayer books. When the service was over I came down from the vestry to shake hands with the worshippers. They always waited for this custom to be observed. They had been shaking hands with my predecessor for more than thirty years and I was expected to follow his example every Wednesday morning. It was part of the ritual.

This Wednesday, Miss Mabel Davies, spinster of the parish of Abergelly all her life, ventured a remark which made me recant my unspoken scorn for the elderly as participants in another Pentecost.

'I hear you are hoping to put up a church on that new council estate,' she said.

'We are indeed,' I replied. 'Actually, we have been offered a temporary building already.'

'You know whose land that used to be,' she went on. 'It belonged to the Earl of Duffryn who gave it to the council over thirty years ago. He owned most of the land around here. It was his father who gave the money to build this church. It's a pity he died a few years ago. He might have done something to help build a real church.'

'Is there a successor?' I asked eagerly.

'Yes. He lives down in the West Country somewhere. I don't think he has the same interest in this part of the world as his father did. The council could tell you where he lives, I expect.'

'Thank you for that information, Miss Davies.' I shook her hand warmly. 'It's a great help.'

When I accepted the living the Bishop had told me that there was some money in the diocesan building funds which could be given towards the cost of a new church but that the bulk of the money would have to come from the parish. Since there was no money in the coffers of St Peter's it was going to be a Herculean task to raise enough to pay for a permanent building. The possibility of a large donation from someone like the Earl of Duffryn was a lifeline, a slender one admittedly.

My wife was sceptical when I told her about my conversation with Miss Davies. 'I expect the Earl has his own ecclesiastical commitments down in the West Country. Abergelly might as well be in Abyssinia as far as he is concerned. Why don't you ask your new rural dean if he thinks there is any chance of a sizeable contribution from the noble lord? He has been in this neck of the woods for the past forty years or so. As you know, he is a bigger gossip than any member of the Mothers' Union. If anybody can tell you, he can.'

The Reverend Llewellyn Evans was a native of Carmarthenshire who thought in Welsh and translated it into English. He had a bizarre habit of adding 'ness' to adjectives and converting them into nouns, whether in the pulpit or in conversation. 'Unthinkingness' and 'Unendingness' were examples of his ability to coin new words.

'Rural Dean speaking,' came the reply when I dialled his number. The accent was an attempt at Oxbridge with ecclesiastical overtones, which foundered on the Celtic bed-rock beneath.

'This is the Vicar of Abergelly, Mr Rural Dean. I wonder if you can help me with some information.'

'Yes, of course – if I can, that is.'

'I learnt this morning from one of my parishioners that the late Earl of Duffryn gave the land to the council where the new Brynfelin housing estate has been built and that his successor now lives in the West Country somewhere.'

'Yes, indeed, he does. His father was a great man for the church, like his father before him. He built your church, as you might know. If only there were more like them. Their giving was unspeakable.'

'I was wondering, Mr Rural Dean, if you have the address of the present Earl. I thought I might write to him to see if he would follow in the family footsteps and help build a new church.'

There was a hollow laugh at the other end of the phone. 'Oh, I'm afraid this Earl is not the same as them. They say that his inclination is more for the racecourse than anything else. I think you had better give up any idea of subsidising-ness from him. I should think that most of your money for the new church will have to come from your own parishion-ers. Looking at your parish details in the diocesan hand-book, you haven't all that many on your electrical roll, have you?'

'I'm afraid we haven't, Mr Rural Dean.'

'Well, I suppose there wouldn't be any harm in writing to the Earl and asking for some help for you in your predicate. It so happens that I have his address here from when we were needing a new organ here in Llansaint. I can tell you now that we had no forthcomingness from him. Perhaps you will be more lucky – blessed, shall I say.'

That was a favourite phrase of his: 'Shall I say' punctuated his pulpit oratory like the currants in Welsh cakes.

There was a long pause while he searched through the drawers of his desk to find the correspondence from the Earl. 'Are you there?' he asked.

'I am still here, Mr Rural Dean,' I said.

'Oh! Good!' he replied. 'At first I thought the phone had gone dead. Well, the address is The Earl of Duffryn, Somerton Castle, Little Trentham, Devon. I hope you have more luck than I did. Let me know how you got on, will you? After all, his ancestors made their money out of exploitingness of this part of the world, didn't they? And if you've taken something out, then you should put something back in. It's only fair, isn't it?' He put down the receiver before I could thank him and acknowledge the truth of his moralising.

'Well?' asked my wife when I came out from the study, 'what did his reverendness have to say? From the look on your face nothing of an encouraging nature, I presume.'

'Your presumption is quite correct, I'm afraid. It seems that the new Earl of Duffryn is more at home at the racecourse than in church. However, I now have his address and I shall write to him, however big the odds against.'

'That is what is known as a long shot, Frederick. Better that than nothing. By the way, in addition to writing that letter, would you please write out an advertisement for a "daily" to send to the paper? If it is as successful as the one for a receptionist, I shall be very happy. Betty Thomas looks as if she is going to be a great help in the surgery.'

'While I am at it,' I replied, 'I may as well write to the Bishop to ask if there is any possibility of me having a Curate. With a new church to be built, I need an assistant now, not in the distant future. The population in the parish has grown considerably. I think his lordship owes it to me to provide one.'

'Quite right, my love. Go for it, Secombe. Insist on having a curate, as long as he is not like the parish's one-and-only specimen in the distant past.'

The one-and-only specimen was the Reverend Augustus Bale, a bachelor with private means who never advanced to the status of incumbent but stayed in Abergelly for twenty-three years until his death in 1931. Always dressed in black and wearing a shovel hat, he was an assiduous visitor who embarrassed members of the congregation by sitting in silence in their homes for long periods and frequently falling asleep. A deep-dyed Evangelical, he demanded that his housekeeper did no cooking on a Sunday. It was a great joke in the parish since everybody knew that she removed the smell of cooking on the sabbath by opening all the doors and windows of the house, while the Reverend Bale was at church. There was a memorial tablet in the chancel which paid tribute to his 'piety and dedication'. It described him as 'a man of God much loved by all who knew him'.

I spent the next morning drafting a letter to the Earl in which I referred to the great debt the parish of Abergelly owed to his family.

It was only through their generosity that the splendid parish church was built in the last century. The need was there and they met it nobly. Today there is a similar

31

need for another church to serve a large population, devoid of a place of worship. Parishioners are girding themselves to face the challenge but with the huge cost of building nowadays it is something they cannot manage on their own. The diocese is unable to contribute a great amount so we are appealing to all those who had any connection with Abergelly to help us in our gigantic task.

To the Bishop, I wrote a simple, straightforward letter pointing out the urgency of the situation I found myself in, without any assistance, whereas in Pontywen, with its much smaller population, I was helped by a curate and a layreader. I found myself saying a silent prayer as I put three letters in the postbox.

The first answer to my prayer came via the local newspaper two days later. There was a ring on the doorbell in the late afternoon. A small thin lady, apparently in her late middle age, stood in the porch. She had brilliant blue eyes which were at variance with her sallow complexion. Although it was a warm spring day, she wore a long brown overcoat which almost reached her ankles. She smiled nervously, revealing a set of National Health teeth.

'I've come about the advert in tonight's paper,' she said.

'That's quick work,' I replied. 'Come on in, please and I'll get my wife to have a word.' I ushered her into the lounge and went into the kitchen where Eleanor was putting a casserole in the oven. 'Our advert has drawn blood already,' I announced.

'What do you mean?' she said. 'It's a daily I want not a transfusion.'

'Very funny,' I replied. 'Anyway she's awaiting your presence in the lounge.' I went into the study to pore through my books in preparation for the next day's sermons.

Half an hour later, there was a tap on my door and my wife's head next appeared round the corner. 'Would you like to come and meet Mrs Jenkins before she goes? She is going to start work with us next Monday.' She winked at me as she passed on the information.

When I came into the hall, Mrs Jenkins was standing there grinning like a Cheshire cat. 'We have had a long chat,' said Eleanor. 'I am sure she is going to be a great help to me.'

'Glad to hear it,' I replied. 'Welcome to the Vicarage, Mrs Jenkins. I hope you will be very happy with us.'

'Oh, I'm sure I will. This job is just what I've wanted and I'll do my best, I can tell you.' We shook hands and my wife and I stood in the porch and watched her walk down the short drive.

'Satisfied with her?' I enquired.

'Like Betty Thomas, I'm sure she is going to be a great help. She is a widow. Her husband died a few years ago. Since then she has been doing school meals and a little bit of housework here and there. She looks to me to be a good worker and conscientious. She doesn't live far away. That's a big advantage.'

'Fine,' I said. 'The next answer will be from the Bishop, I hope, and just as favourable as this one has been.'

She kissed me. 'I feel it in my bones that it will be.'

'I hope you're right,' I said.

She was right, as usual. The reply came not by letter but via the telephone that evening. We had just finished our dinner and I was about to go upstairs to read to my son before he went to sleep.

'You go on up, love,' Eleanor said when the phone rang. 'I'll answer it.'

A minute or two later, she came bounding upstairs. 'It's the Bishop,' she shouted excitedly when she was half-way up. I left a bewildered David and almost collided with my wife on my way down.

'What did I tell you,' she said.

'We'll see,' I replied. When I got to the phone, I was panting. 'Good evening, my lord,' I gasped.

'Calm down, Fred,' said the Bishop. 'I am just ringing to say that I have had your letter. I've been away at a conference and arrived back this afternoon. Yes, you certainly need a curate and you can have one. I am afraid that it will have to be a deacon but that will not matter at this stage. I have a young man due for ordination this Trinity, Hugh Thomas. He took a second class degree in History in Cardiff and he has been at St Michael's Llandaff doing his theological training. He is twenty-three years old and is keen to be "fully employed", as he puts it. In other words, he should be just the man you need with all the problems confronting you. I suggest that you write to him at his home address, seven St Leger Crescent, Llangarth, to arrange an interview. He has a pleasant personality and is of more than reasonable intelligence, as his degree indicates. Let me know how you get on with him and if you are prepared to offer him the curacy. I trust this sets your mind at rest.'

I ran upstairs even more quickly than Eleanor's effort earlier on. Before I could burst in on David and his mother, she opened the door, finger on her lips. She closed the door quickly and then kissed me for the second time. 'Don't tell me,' she whispered, 'you are going to have a curate. Let's go

34

downstairs and you can tell me all about it. Two sentences from me and your son was asleep.'

When I had given her all the details which the Bishop had supplied, she said, 'It couldn't be better. You have a young man whom you can train and he will be coming with all the enthusiasm of youth, fresh from college and eager to change the world.'

'All I can say in answer to that, my love, is that if he is eager to change the world he is not going to be easy to train.'

'True enough,' she said.

As we were drinking a celebratory glass of sherry, I said to her, 'I suppose it is too much to hope for to have a third satisfactory reply to my letter. It will take a miracle to have a huge donation from the Earl and a minor miracle to have even a token donation. Still, two out of three in a short space of time is not bad going.'

'I should think if he had two successful bets out of three he would consider himself very lucky,' she replied.

Next morning after service I called the churchwardens into the vestry to pass on the news that the Bishop had offered me a curate. Tom Beynon declared himself delighted. The response from Amos Perkins was predictable. "And where is the money coming from to pay for a curate? With all the burdens you are going to put on our backs you are going to add another one. Don't forget it was only a straw that broke the camel's back. This is much more than a straw.'

'If we are going to talk about camels, Mr Perkins,' I replied, 'I would prefer a quotation from the New Testament. "It is easier for a camel to go through the eye of a needle than for a rich man to enter the kingdom of God". The level of giving in this parish is deplorably low and I intend to do something about it, as I said at the PCC meeting. We shall have help from the diocese and from one of the church societies in paying the curate's stipend. I suggest that we have a PCC meeting next week. There is much to discuss. The setting up of a committee to organise the building of the temporary church on the Brynfelin estate, the organisation of a fundraising campaign and so on.'

We decided to hold the meeting on the Tuesday of the week following. 'I tell you what,' said my warden, 'I think you will find that there will be a lot more opposition to your highfalutin' plans than there was at the first one.'

'Well, Amos,' said Tom Beynon, 'I am the people's warden, not like you who should be supporting the Vicar, in any case, not opposing him. As far as I can tell the congregation are behind our Vicar. I think you will find that out on Tuesday week.'

I could not bring myself to address my warden as 'Amos'. That word would stick in my throat. I knew it was unChristian to feel like that. I found it easy to call the people's warden Tom but the word 'Amos' refused to come from my mouth.

'All I can say, Mr Perkins, is that I hope the meeting will be more concerned to advance the cause of the Kingdom of God in Abergelly than to indulge in an unseemly affair more appropriate to a boxing ring than a fellowship of Christians.'

'Amen,' said Tom Beynon.

3

There was a knock on the back door at nine o'clock the next morning. It heralded the arrival of Mrs Jenkins, with a handful of letters.

'I met Jim the Post at the gate. I told him I would save him a walk up your drive. I hope you don't mind.'

'Not at all, Mrs Jenkins,' I replied. 'By the way, you don't have to come to the back door. We haven't a doorbell there, as you can see. It just happened that I was in the kitchen at the time. Otherwise you could have been waiting for some time before anybody heard you.'

'Right you are, Vicar,' she said. 'I just didn't want to be above myself. Like my mother always used to tell me that you should know your place, if you know what I mean.'

'Well, Mrs Jenkins, your place is here in the Vicarage and you are just as important as anybody else who comes to the front door. Don't forget that.'

At that moment Eleanor appeared. 'Hello, Mrs Jenkins!' she said. 'Let's have a cup of tea before you start work.'

From then on, Mrs Jenkins became an indispensable member of the household.

I went into the study and sorted out the letters on the desk, two for my wife and three for me, two typed and one address handwritten, bearing a Plymouth postmark. When I saw that, like 'Stout Cortes', I stared at it 'with a wild surmise'. As I turned over the envelope to open it, the embossed flap confirmed my excited reaction. 'It's a personal letter,' I said to myself. 'If the Earl was going to turn down my appeal for help, he would have done that via his secretary. This is handwritten and must be from himself.' I opened the letter with the paperknife my parents had given me for my birthday, my hand trembling. 'Mam!' I murmured. 'Bring me luck, there's a dear, please.' As I extracted the expensive note-paper, I could hardly bring myself to unfold it. With my heart hammering, I began to read the almost indecipherable scrawl:

My dear Vicar,

Thank you for your very interesting letter with its details about the connection between my family and your parish. I did not know that my forebears had been responsible for the building of your church. It seems from what you say, that there is urgent need for another church to serve the growing population. May I suggest that you come down here to see me when we can have a tête-à-tête about the matter. If it is convenient to you, Wednesday 12th June would be suitable for me. Perhaps you would kindly let me know if this is agreeable to you.

Yours sincerely,
James Davenport Herbert,
Earl of Duffryn.

I read the letter a second time before dashing out into the kitchen. 'It's worked,' I shouted, waving the letter in the air.

'You must excuse my husband,' said Eleanor to Mrs Jenkins, 'he gets turns like this occasionally. What has worked, dear?'

'My letter to the Earl. He wants to see me on the twelfth of June.'

'You must excuse us for a moment while we go into the study. If you want any more tea, there's plenty in the pot.'

She put her arm round my back and led me into the study. 'You mustn't frighten the servants like that, Frederick. Otherwise they will think you are deranged and seek employment elsewhere. You lucky old thing! He has taken the bait.' I gave her the letter. As she began to read, she said, 'He has missed his vocation. He could write some fascinating prescriptions.' When she had finished, she gave me a hug. 'The Lord must be with you, my sweetheart,' she whispered in my ear.

'Both of them, I hope,' I replied.

'Very witty, not to mention corny. Back to the kitchen. By the way, she is going to be a treasure.'

'Oh! What a beautiful morning,' she began to sing and continued to do so until she reached the kitchen door.

That afternoon, with tides of euphoria washing over me, I set out to see Jack Richards at his fish and chip shop in Monmouth Road. He was a short, stout, red-faced man with a countenance more appropriate behind a bar counter than at the steaming-range in his premises.

'Come on in, Vicar,' he said. 'Tom Beynon told me you would be coming to see me.' He led me through the shop and into the living room at the back. The stale smell of frying hung like a pall over the living room as much as in the shop. When I sat in an armchair by the fireplace, that piece of furniture stank so much that my stomach began to turn over. I was determined to make the interview as short as possible and invent a plausible excuse for a quick exit.

'Tom Beynon said you would be coming to see me about this temporary building, up on the new housing estate.' His speech was punctuated by an occasional wheeze, like my grandfather's. I wondered how much the frying was responsible for his chest condition. 'It's years since I was in the building trade. Mind, you never forget what you have learnt. I started when I was fourteen working for my father, who was a builder up by your old parish. It'll do me good to be out in the open air for a bit. When is this pre-fab due to be delivered to the site?'

'Whenever we are ready to get to work on it,' I replied.

'The first thing is to get the site prepared,' he said. 'So the sooner we start on that the better.'

'There's a PCC meeting a week tomorrow to get a working committee appointed. Obviously, as the man in charge of the operations, you will have to be on it.'

'Bugger the committee!' he said. 'All committees do is talk. What I want is men who know what they are doing working with me. Tom has told me that we have got a good team in the making. Well, I'm ready as soon as you give me the go-ahead.'

I took that as a signal to get up and to escape from that all-pervading aroma of Jack's second trade.

'Would you like something to drink, Vicar?'

'No thanks, Mr Richards. I've got a lot of visiting to do this afternoon.'

'Well, on your way then, Vicar. By the way call, me Jack, please, not Mr Richards. Everybody else does.'

'Right you are, Jack. I'll be in touch next week sometime. You are on the phone, aren't you?' If I could avoid another visit to the house so much the better.

'Of course, Abergelly three five seven. You'll find it in the directory under 'Jack's Fish Bar'. I was going to ask where the bar came in, but decided against it in my haste to get away.

I went straight back to the Vicarage to change my suit. As soon as I came through the door, my beloved said, 'You ain't half ponging, love. You have been visiting "Jack's Fish Bar", haven't you? Open all the windows upstairs when you change and leave your suit on that clothes horse in the back bedroom, by the open window, please.'

When I came downstairs she said, 'While you were out, I had a phone call from your new curate-to-be, thanking you for your letter and saying that he would be delighted to be your sidekick.'

'I don't think he said that, love,' I interrupted.

'No, he didn't, but that is what he is, isn't he. Anyway, he wondered when he might come down to meet you. He has a telephone number which I have put on the notepad on your desk.'

'A telephone number,' I exclaimed. 'That's more than I had when I was an ordinand. How times change!'

'For the better, I trust, Frederick. I had a telephone number when I was his age.'

'But you didn't live on a council estate, did you?'

'Stop playing that violin, Secombe. It doesn't suit you. It's much more important that you go to the study and phone him. He sounds like a very nice young man. It seems you are going to be lucky again or well blessed, if you want to put it that way.'

'Yes, I think I prefer it put that way.'

I rang the number on the notepad.

41

'Hugh Thomas speaking,' came the reply. The tone of his voice oozed self-confidence.

'The Vicar of Abergelly here,' I said. 'I understand from my wife that you would be pleased to become my assistant and that you would like to come down to meet me.'

'Very much so, Vicar. The Bishop has told me of the big challenge you are facing in Abergelly. I love a challenge and I should love to be part of your front-line action strategy. I know I have a lot to learn but where better to do that than in the front line.'

'Well, Hugh,' I replied, 'I think the sooner you come down to survey the battlefield the better. Do you think you will be able to visit us on Thursday morning, say, at eleven o'clock?'

'I'll be there on the dot, Vicar. By the way, is there anywhere to park my car?'

There was a silence while I strove to come to terms with the fact that my twenty-three-year-old curate was the owner of a car. 'You have a car, Hugh?' I said eventually.

'It's only an old banger but it is pretty reliable,' he replied cheerily. 'It will be enough to get me around the parish until I can afford a better one.'

'If you are going to rely on your stipend I am afraid that will be quite a while. Anyway we can discuss your stipend and other matters when you come on Thursday. I shall leave room for your old banger in the Vicarage drive. See you then.'

'Thank you, Vicar. I look forward to meeting you.'

I went back to the kitchen where my wife was about to take a cake out of the oven. 'Look at that, Fred – the cut-and-come-again cake your mother makes.'

As she put it on the table, I said, 'Well done, that girl. It's the best you've ever made.'

'I have to confess, lord and master, that I did not make it. It is Mrs Jenkins' first culinary effort. I think you will find the currants evenly distributed and not clinging to each other in large numbers as in the Eleanor recipe. We have definitely scored a hit by employing her. I hope the same thing applies to your new curate.'

'Time will tell,' I replied.

'You don't sound very enthusiastic, dear,' she said. 'I thought he was very nice when he rang up – chirpy and full of life. What makes you so cagey?'

'I am not quite sure whether this parish is the place for him. He wanted to know if there was anywhere he could park his car when he comes on Thursday. I get the impression that he is over-confident because of his affluent background and that before long he would be attempting to run the parish. What's more, I don't know how he would get on with the people on the council estate. It will be a different world for him. I grew up in that world.'

'Secombe!' she exploded. 'You have a chip on your shoulder and the sooner you get rid of it the better. How dare you condemn this young man because he happens to have been brought up in a different context from yours. Because he is on the phone and has a car, you assume that he is living on Mars, a creature from space. Wait till you meet him and then make your judgement.'

'All right, you win. I suppose I am jumping the gun. There's one other thing, we shall have to find "digs" for him. That is not going to be easy. I expect he will be very choosey.'

43

'Back you go to square one! I am sure he will be grateful for whatever lodgings you get for him and I am certain you will do your best in that respect. Tom Beynon seems to know everybody in Abergelly. If you ask him, you can't go wrong. Have a word with him tomorrow and if he knows anybody perhaps you can go and see for yourself what the place is like before your new man comes on Thursday.'

'Better still,' I said, 'once we have had our corned beef hash *à la* Eleanor recipe, followed by a piece of cake *à la* Jenkins recipe, I'll pop down and see him. The sooner we have things sorted out the better.'

'What a man of action you are, Frederick,' she replied.

Later that evening, with a mixture of corned beef hash and currant cake swirling around in my stomach, I made my way to Tom Beynon's residence. 'Two visits inside seven days,' he exclaimed when he saw me. 'That's more than the old vicar made in twelve months. Pleased to see you, Vicar. Come on in and share a jar with me.'

As we drank our beer, I explained the purpose of my visit. 'Offhand, I can only think of one landlady for him. That's Mrs Rogers, Raglan House, just round the corner from here. She takes in lodgers and she has just had Kevin Howells from Lloyds Bank leave her to work in Cardiff. He had his own sitting room, except on Thursdays when the dentist comes from Newport for his surgery. He's got his equipment in the front room and uses the little middle room as a waiting place for his patients. Apart from Thursdays, that room is vacant all the week. She's got two or three lodgers and everybody has meals down in the basement. Mrs Williams is a very good cook and is very clean and tidy, regular in church, too. She's about the only one I can think of at the moment, if that's any use.'

'That's fine, Tom,' I replied. 'I'll call round there tomorrow morning first thing just in case she has let the room.'

Next day, at nine o'clock I was pressing the button of the 'Raglan House' doorbell. It was a three-storied house, recently redecorated in black and white. An immaculately polished brass plate at the side of the door bore the name of D. M. Alabaster, LDS. There was no response. I tried once again and waited. I was about to go away and call back later when I heard heavy footsteps scurrying along the hall. A large lady appeared, puffing and blowing, her ample figure adorned with a postage stamp of an apron. She peered at me through her horn-rimmed spectacles. Then an embarrassed smile flickered on her countenance.

'Vicar! How nice to see you. Would you like to come in?' As we made our way to the little middle room, she apologised for her appearance. 'I was just about to do the beds. To be honest I'm not used to having visitors this time of the morning.'

'It's my turn to apologise, Mrs Rogers. I don't normally go visiting at this hour, but my mission is urgent. I understand that you have a small sitting room and bedroom vacant. At least I hope so.'

'Please, sit down, Vicar. Yes, I have indeed. I was going to put an advert in the paper tomorrow.' She sat down opposite me, nervously fingering the top of her jumper. 'This is the sitting room but I've got to tell you that it's not available on Thursdays. That's the day that Mr Alabaster the dentist comes up from Newport to do his surgery. I expect you saw

45

his brass plate by the door. He's got all his machinery and things in the front room and his patients wait here. Apart from that the room is available all the other days of the week. I've got three other lodgers and we all have our evening meals and breakfast down in the basement. There's a fair sized room on the first floor where there's a bathroom and lavatory. If you don't mind me asking, Vicar, who's it for?'

'In a few weeks' time, Mrs Rogers, the parish is going to have a curate and I need to find somewhere for him to live. Tom Beynon suggested that you might be able to help and from what you tell me it seems that this would be an ideal place.'

Her eyes opened wide. 'A curate. We haven't had one of them since old Mr Bale. I can just about remember him when I was a little girl. I hope he is not going to be like him.'

'No, Mrs Rogers, he is a young man, just out of college, twenty-three years old and full of the joys of spring.'

'Well, Vicar, if he wants to come here, he will be very welcome. Two of my paying guests are young ladies and I'm sure they will be more than happy to have his company at the table for meals. I expect all the other young ladies at church will be glad to see him.'

'All I can say in answer to that is he may be engaged, I don't know. I trust, for his sake, that he has a fiancée. He is coming here to see me on Thursday. I shall find out then. Is it convenient for me to bring him round that afternoon?'

'With pleasure, Vicar. I will try to look more presentable by then. Would you like a cup of tea or coffee before you go?'

'No, thank you, you have enough to do as it is. Perhaps next Thursday when I bring your new lodger.'

'Oh, by the way, Vicar, my husband is a signalman and works in the box at the Pontywen junction. So I heard a lot about you before you came here. All good, I can tell you that.'

'It's just as well, Mrs Rogers. Otherwise my reputation would have been ruined before I came here. I expect he knew Jack Hughes, one of my sidesmen in Pontywen, who works there.'

'Yes, that's where he had it all from. He was very sorry to see you go and what's more he said that they are all sorry for the new man when he is chosen. It won't be easy to follow in your footsteps.'

'I don't think so, once he gets settled in and takes over the congregations will rally round him and he will soon be the Vicar of Pontywen in his own right, making his own mark on the parish, irrespective of Fred Secombe, I can tell you.'

I had just turned the corner from Raglan House when an ancient Morris Minor pulled up alongside me. At the wheel was a large man and moving around on the back seat was a large greyhound. The driver wound his window down.

'I'm Dai Rees,' he announced in a basso profundo voice. 'Tom Beynon tells me you would like my help with the electrics, when you put up this pre-fab church on the Bryn-felin estate.'

I was about to say, 'You must be Dai Elbow' but strangled the comment at birth in case I felt the impact of his elbow. 'You must be the gentleman who is an electrician at the colliery,' I said instead.

'Hop in, Vicar, and take a seat for a minute so I can give

47

you a lift back to the Vicarage, if you like. I'm going past there on my way to the Vet's.'

'That's very kind, Mr Rees. I'll accept your offer, I want to get back as soon as possible. I've got loads of things to do today.'

Like the lion who swallowed Albert in Stanley Holloway's monologue, I was sorry the moment I did it. As soon as I got into the seat, I was showered with kisses from behind.

'Don't take any notice of her, Vic,' advised Dai Elbow. 'She's very affectionate. I didn't buy her as a pet. I wanted a bitch who could win races not one who could only give kisses. She's got a pedigree as long as your arm and she's come last in every race so far. She's more interested in the other dogs than the hare. I'm going to the Vet's to see if he can give her something to concentrate on winning as I used to do when I played rugby. Anyway, what I want to tell you is that I will be pleased to see to all the electrics and to help with a bit of manual labour. I'm still fit and some exercise will do me no 'arm. By the way, call me "Dai" please. I don't answer to the name of Mr Rees and I am not a gentleman.' Since he had addressed me as 'Vic', I supposed it was only fair that I reciprocated with 'Dai'.

By now we had stopped outside the Vicarage drive. I opened the car door and leant across to shake hands with him. As I did so the dog became a hurdler. She leapt over my shoulder and disappeared up the drive, trailing her lead behind her at a speed which would win any race.

'Bloody 'ell,' exclaimed Dai. He was out of the car in a split second. 'Shut your gates, Vic,' he shouted. I obeyed but as I did so, I wondered if that would be effective, considering the way she cleared my shoulder. As I watched the burly figure lumbering around the front of the Vicarage, I looked up to see my wife in the front window of the sitting room, apparently suffering from paroxysms of laughter. 'Bella,' boomed the bass voice which must have been heard echoing around the town centre of Abergelly. The chase ended in the gravel of the drive directly opposite the sitting room with a rugby tackle cleaner than any elbowing perfected by Dai. My wife was no longer to be seen. She had either gone to invite Mrs Jenkins to view the scene or she had collapsed on the settee in the bay window.

Clasping the dog's lead with an iron grip, Dai hauled the animal towards the car, muttering *sotto voce* curses on the way.

'Sorry about this, Vic,' he said. 'It's the wife's fault. What's the point of me trying to train 'er, when she spoils 'er behind my back. I don't think it's the Vet I ought to be seeing but a bloody magician. She's supposed to be running at Newport tomorrow. Another waste of time and petrol, I expect.'

'I tell you what, Dai,' I replied, 'if she runs as fast as she did a minute ago, she'll win that race by yards.'

He laughed a hollow laugh. 'That'll be the day.' He pushed the hound into the car. 'Would you believe it,' he exclaimed, 'she's being sick!'

'Shall I get something from the Vicarage to mop it up?' I asked, adding a silent prayer of thanks that I was not in the front seat.

'No, it's all right, Vic,' he sighed. 'I've got a cloth here. I'll mop it when I get to the Vet's. See you soon up at Brynfelin.' He slammed the door, put his foot on the accelerator and the dog promptly vomitted on the back seat.

Before I could open the front door, my wife was there before me, with tears of laughter lingering around her eyes.

'Who on earth was that?' she breathed. 'He'd make a small fortune as a circus act. Give him a large red nose, a wig and a pair of baggy trousers and he'd top the bill.'

'That, my dear,' I replied, 'was Dai Elbow, the most feared forward in Abergelly.'

'I could see that by the way he captured that poor dog. Between them they have taken away most of the gravel on our drive,' she said.

'What you don't realise, is that Bella, the dog, is a greyhound with an impressive pedigree.'

'Frederick, I could see that when she darted around the house.'

'What you also do not realise is the fact that she is always last in every race because she is more interested in bestowing kisses than racing. In the two minutes it took Dai to drive me from Raglan House I received enough facial treatment to keep me clean for a fortnight. He is taking her to the Vet to see if he can transform her from a sex symbol into a dedicated athlete.'

'How on earth did you come to be in the car with those two?' she enquired.

'He pulled up alongside me as I was coming from the future digs for the new curate, to inform me that he will be pleased to do the electrics in the new church and even to help with the manual labour.'

'By his size,' she said, 'I should think he would be a great help in that respect.'

'Oh, and another thing,' I added, 'he has given me a new title – "Vic".'

'I know they shorten everybody's name in the valleys but I think Vic takes the biscuit,' she commented.

'What's more important?' I went on, 'is the news that I have found suitable digs for the curate. Raglan House sounds sufficiently impressive as the abode for an affluent curate. From the little I saw of it, the house seems to be very clean and from the little I saw of the landlady she seems to be in the same category. Mrs Rogers is a plump, jovial lady in her early fifties, I should say, with a ready smile and with bannister legs.'

'Vic, to coin a word, I don't believe it. You were looking at her legs.'

'My dear Eleanor, I don't make a point of looking at ladies' legs, but hers were of a very unusual shape, normally seen on a staircase.'

'I don't think she would be flattered to hear you describe them in that way. However, as you say, what matters is that you have got a place for him. What would you do without Tom Beynon?'

'There's only one thing,' I added, 'and that is we shall have to provide him with meals on Thursday when the dentist comes to town, taking over his sitting room.'

'Why don't you make Thursday his day off,' she said. 'His parents live fairly near and he has a car. I am sure he will be able to relax more in his own home than here where inevitably you would be talking shop.'

'Quite right, oh wise one,' I replied. 'Why doesn't God give me common sense in the same quantity he bestows upon you.'

'Don't ask me, love, you are the parson. I'm just the doctor. Now then, if you don't mind, I have to get on with my work. I am meeting my new receptionist at my new surgery in half an hour. Marlene has taken the children out to the park and Mrs Jenkins is making lunch for us, amongst other things. So you go your way and I'll go mine and we'll meet at one o'clock.'

She gave me a peck on the cheek and went to the garage to get her car. A minute or so later there was a roar of the engine. Eleanor loved to rev up before driving off. As I looked out through my study window I could see the fumes from the exhaust which always heralded her departure, as if she was on the starting line at Brand's Hatch. The scene was interrupted by the ringing of the telephone.

'Cynthia Rogers here, Vicar,' proclaimed the voice at the other end. 'Excuse me for calling you; did you say that you were bringing the new curate next Thursday?'

'I did indeed, Mrs Rogers,' I replied.

'Well, if you don't mind, could you make it another day, please. Mr Alabaster will be here for his surgery, so I wouldn't be able to show the curate his sitting room and, apart from that, I would be too busy to see him. I'm so sorry, Vicar. I don't know what made me forget that.'

'It's my fault as much as yours. After all our conversation

about Thursdays, I should have realised that. The fact of the matter is that I had arranged for him to come and see me on that day before I knew about your vacancy. I'll ring him straight away and change the day to Friday, if that is convenient.'

'That will be fine, Vicar. He'll be able to meet my husband as well. He's working mornings that day.'

When I rang the number on my notepad, I was surprised to hear that it was 'Doctor Mervyn Thomas speaking'.

'This is Fred Secombe, Vicar of Abergelly. Could I speak to Hugh Thomas, please?'

'Good morning, Vicar, this is Hugh's father. I'm afraid he is out at the moment. He and a couple of his pals are having a morning net practice at the cricket club. Apparently there is an important match on Saturday and they want to get in trim. He will be back lunchtime. I have to go out on my rounds now but I shall leave a message for him to ring you. I understand that your good lady is a doctor. Actually I knew her father quite well. We were in college together. I was hoping that Hugh would follow in my footsteps as your wife did. However, it seems that he would rather have a dog collar round his neck than a stethoscope. He could do worse, I suppose. I look forward to meeting you one of these days – at his ordination, if not before then.'

When I put down the receiver, my future curate's affluence had been explained and what was more his personality had taken on a new dimension. None of my previous assistants had any sporting ability, just like myself. I had to cope with a young man in comparison with whom I was a non-event physically. The moment of truth had arrived for me.

When Eleanor arrived home for lunch, I said, 'I have news for you, *ma petite*.'

'Less of the "*petite*",' she replied, 'you're not much bigger than I am. Well, what is the earth-shattering announcement?'

'Our new curate is the son of a doctor. Dr Mervyn Thomas, to be precise.'

'Would you never? He used to be one of my father's student friends. My dad often used to speak of him. It seems he was a bit of a wag.'

'He still is. According to him, his son would prefer a dog collar round his neck instead of stethoscope.'

'Let's hope his son has his family sense of humour,' said my wife.

Halfway through our lunch the telephone rang.

'Hugh Thomas here. I'm sorry I was not here when you rang earlier, Vicar, but I had a prior engagement.'

'At the cricket nets, I gather,' I replied.

'You have been talking to my father, evidently. In any case, Vicar, what can I do for you?' He sounded more than a little annoyed.

'Well, Hugh, I wonder if you can come down here on Friday instead of Thursday. Your future landlady will not be able to show you around until then. So, if you come to Abergelly at eleven o'clock, I shall be able to take you around the parish, provide lunch for you here at the Vicarage and introduce you to your landlady and her husband, in the early afternoon.'

'At your service, sir. I shall look forward to meeting you at eleven a.m. precisely.'

There was a mocking tone in that reply which made me

wonder whether I had made the wrong choice of a curate for the third time, excluding, of course, the excellent man I had left behind in Pontywen, Emlyn Howells. How I wished that Emlyn could have come with me, an ex-miner and in his thirties. Instead I was to be saddled with a twenty-three-year-old, afflicted by an overdose of self-confidence and brought up in a middle-class home, far removed from the council houses of the Brynfelin estate.

4

It was eleven a.m. precisely on Friday but there was no sign of Hugh Thomas. At 11.15 the telephone rang.

'My apologies, Vicar,' said my curate-to-be. 'I'm ringing from a callbox on the Newport road. I'm afraid my car has broken down. I've called the AA and they say they will be with me as soon as possible, whenever that is. Ah, well, *c'est la vie*.' For someone who had offered his apologies he sounded very unapologetic. 'Thank you for ringing, Hugh,' I replied. 'I have plenty to do while I wait for you, like writing copy for this month's magazine, for example.'

'I can help you there, Vicar. I used to edit the college magazine. It's one of my strong points. Got to go, the AA have just turned up, would you believe it.'

Half an hour later, an MG sports car made a noisy entrance into the drive. I went to the front door to receive my visitor. To my surprise, instead of the tall blond figure I had imagined, a short, stocky, swarthy, dark-haired young man ran up the steps. 'Sorry, I'm late, Vicar,' he said and thrust out his hand. 'As I think I told you, my steed is feeling the effects of old age. So the sooner I get a replacement the better. Thank God for the AA, I say. Oh! that rhymes, doesn't it?'

Evidently he was following in his father's footsteps as something of a wag, but if that witticism was an example I feared for our relationship.

When he came into my study, he surveyed the books which lined the walls. 'Much more up to date than our Vicar's library at home,' he commented. 'I think Noah must have given them to him when he vacated the Ark. He's as old as that.' He looked at me to see if I was impressed by his sense of humour. When he failed to observe any trace of amusement on my face, he coughed and seated himself on the chair opposite my desk.

'I'll get us some coffee,' I said, and went out to the kitchen where Mrs Jenkins was preparing lunch.

'It's all ready, Vicar,' she assured me. 'That pergulator's been bubbling away for ages. I've put some biscuits out on a plate and the milk and sugar's on the tray. By the way, Dr Secombe said she would be back by one o'clock for lunch. Marlene is bringing the children back by half-past twelve and I've got their dinner ready for them.'

'Thank you, Mrs Jenkins,' I replied. 'Do you want me to bring the tray to the study?' she asked.

'I think I can manage that,' I said.

'Now, then,' I said as we sat drinking our coffee. 'So you would like to be Curate of Abergelly. That will be a tough assignment. We have a large population to serve. All we have to offer at the moment is a church badly in need of decoration, a church hall even more so and an empty plot of ground in the middle of a new housing estate. I need a man who is prepared to roll up his sleeves and indulge in a lot of sweated labour. If you are prepared to do that, the curacy is yours. If not, then you had better look elsewhere for a less demanding parish.'

He looked me in the eyes. 'I told you when I phoned you that I like a challenge, Vicar, and I am certainly ready to roll up my sleeves. In that case, may I take it that the curacy is mine?' Ten minutes later we were inspecting the interior of the church.

'I like it but I see what you mean about its poor state of decoration,' he murmured.

'Wait until you see the church hall,' I said.

He began to whistle his dismay as soon as he saw the battered door and the peeling paint on the window frames. Once inside, his eyes opened wide as he surveyed the extent of the damage done by damp to the walls and the ceilings.

'You weren't exaggerating, Vicar, when you talked about the need for repairs and decoration. Still, there's one thing. It's a big building and as far as I can see the structure's OK. All it wants is a hundred per cent face lift. I did my National Service with the Royal Engineers and I learnt a lot about buildings in those two years. It should come in handy if you are going to tackle the problems with voluntary labour, as you say.'

By now, I was beginning to revise my assessment of my new assistant's capabilities.

'The next stage of our tour of the parish is a visit to the Brynfelin housing estate,' I said when we went back to the Vicarage. 'Well, since my car is blocking your drive, may I invite you to a ride in my tin lizzy, Vicar?' he replied.

'I would hardly call an MG a tin lizzy, but I should be delighted to accept your offer.'

I climbed into the front seat alongside him. He ostentatiously adjusted his cravat and tucked it inside the open shirt adorned by his college blazer. The next minute we were out of the drive and out on the main road.

'You guide me, Vicar,' he commanded.

'In the first place, you are going in the wrong direction,' I said. 'You had better turn left at the next street and from there on, perhaps if you drove a little more slowly, I would have a chance to point you in the right direction.'

He laughed and then apologised. 'My father always says that I go at anything like a bull at a gate. Perhaps you can teach me to be different.'

'I'll try,' I said.

Soon we were on the top of the hill overlooking Abergelly, surrounded by endless terraces of look-alike boxes. 'This is where two thousand people live,' I told him. 'They have been dumped in no-man's land without a thought of where they are to shop or live together as a community. They have just as much relevance to the council as the rubbish tips up the valley.'

We were standing on the weed-ridden plot of land when a young woman came up to us, with a baby wrapped in a shawl around her, 'Welsh fashion', as it was said at that time. A little boy of about three years old was holding on to her skirt.

'Can you tell me if the bus has gone?' she enquired. 'It's supposed to be here at a quarter to one. I was a bit late coming out of the 'ouse but I 'oped it would be late. It very often is.'

I looked at my watch. 'It's ten to one, I'm afraid. Perhaps we can give you a lift into Abergelly if my driver is willing.'

'By all means,' he replied enthusiastically. 'We shall all have to squeeze in, if you don't mind.'

For the next quarter of an hour I had the little boy on my lap while the mother was jammed between me and the door. It was a warm May afternoon and the body odour exuding from our fellow travellers was overpowering, despite the open top of the MG. 'Thank you ever so much,' said the young lady to Hugh when we arrived in the town centre.

'Only too pleased,' he replied. 'Perhaps I shall be seeing you when I come visiting one of these days. You see, I shall be the Vicar's curate before long and we shall be putting up a church here soon.'

'Fancy that,' she said and went off quickly with her offspring.

'She didn't sound very enthusiastic,' he commented.

'I should think that will be about par for the course, I'm afraid, Hugh,' I replied.

By the time we had returned to the Vicarage, Eleanor was back and helping Mrs Jenkins in the kitchen. 'I thought you would have been home long before now,' she said. 'I'm afraid it's my fault, Mrs Secombe,' replied our guest. 'My car broke down on my way here and I had to phone the AA for assistance – a loose connection apparently. So I was late arriving.'

'Well, let's hope, Mr Thomas, that you will not have any loose connections when you come to Abergelly.' She shook his hand. 'Please forgive that facetious remark, Hugh. You will find that I am given to such lapses. How nice to meet you, especially since your father was an acquaintance of my father during their college days. Ask him if he remembers Jack Davies.'

That was the prelude to a very convivial lunch after which I took my future colleague to meet his landlady.

Mrs Cynthia Rogers had prepared herself and her house with great care for the visit of her new lodger. Her face bore evidence of an excessive application of a powder puff and lipstick, whilst there had been similar applications of her furniture polish which assaulted our nostrils when she opened the front door. She was wearing a floral dress and was sporting a pair of earrings which were almost in contact with her shoulders. A side-long glance at Hugh made me aware that he was struggling to keep a straight face. 'So this is our new Curate,' she gushed. 'Welcome to Raglan House. I hope you will be very happy here.'

'Thank you, Mrs Rogers,' he said. 'I am looking forward to coming here, especially since the Vicar has told me that you are such a good cook. I love my food.'

'Thank you, Vicar, for giving me such a good reference. I do try to give my paying guests every satisfaction. I suppose you would call it making a home for them where they can eat well and sleep well. I do my best anyway.'

'You can't do any more than your best, Mrs Rogers,' I said.

'Well, don't let's stand here,' she replied. 'First of all, you must come and meet my husband.'

She led us downstairs to the basement where a little bald-headed man was seated in a rocking chair at the side of the fireplace. He shot forwards out of the chair as we came into the room.

'Evan,' she said, 'this is our new paying guest, Mr – er.'

'I'm Hugh Thomas, Mr Rogers,' announced the new 'paying guest'.

Evan smiled a gap-toothed smile. He was a bad advertisement for Mr Alabaster, the dentist.

'Pleased to meet you, Mr Thomas.' His lack of teeth gave him a pronounced lisp. 'I hope you can play dominoes. I haven't had a game since Kevin left. The girls can't play for nuts.'

'I'm afraid I'm in the same category, Mr Rogers,' he

replied. 'My games are cricket and rugby. I'm an outdoors man.' Evans' face fell.

When we had finished our tour of the house, including a brief incursion into Mr Alabaster's chamber of horrors, we went down again to the basement where a tray, decorated with a lace cloth and containing three cups and saucers plus accessories, was placed on the large table which dominated the room.

'I've boiled the kettle, Cynth,' lisped her husband.

Hugh declared himself very pleased with what he had seen, as Mrs Rogers poured the tea into her best china. 'I'm sorry about the Thursdays,' she said. 'Perhaps you can have that as your day off.'

He looked at me. 'I'm hoping the Vicar will let me have Saturday as my day off. I play cricket for our local team and I have been invited to have a trial for Abergelly Rugby Club next August.'

'We'll talk about that when we go back to the Vicarage,' I said. 'More importantly at this moment is how much a week do you charge for his upkeep, Mrs Rogers?'

'Kevin used to pay me four pounds a week. Is that all right, Mr Thomas?'

'That's fine by me,' he replied. 'May I pay you on a monthly basis? I understand from the Vicar that I shall be paid monthly.'

'Kevin used to get his wages monthly at the bank. So I am used to that,' said Mrs Rogers. I had told Hugh that his stipend for his first year, as a deacon, would be two hundred and fifty pounds per annum, with a possible rise to three hundred pounds when he was priested. Certainly during his first year, he would have very little to put aside to replace his old 'banger'.

As we sat in my study, prior to his departure, I raised the question of his day off. 'It seems that you would like to have Saturday as your day off. For your first year I am agreeable to that since you will be unable to take any weddings as a deacon. However, after that from time to time I may need your help, especially if there is a rush of couples to beat the April tax barrier by marrying in March.'

'Fair enough, Vicar,' he replied. 'The rugby season will be almost over by then.'

'As far as Thursdays are concerned, I suggest you come here for the day and have your meals with us.'

'That is very kind, Vicar, and much appreciated. I am sure that my time at Abergelly is going to be a very happy one and I promise that I shall do my utmost best in the parish, come what may.'

'I assure you, Hugh, that there will be plenty of "come what mays" and that there will be many disappointments as well as triumphs but if you are going to do "your utmost best" then you can't do any more than that.'

Five minutes later, after he had gone, there was a ring of the door bell. I had just begun the Vicar's letter for the parish magazine. 'Four o'clock in the afternoon,' I muttered. 'What a time to call!'

I opened the door to find an unshaven, unkempt individual, obviously a 'knight of the road', who appeared to be in dire distress.

'I've got the DTs, Reverend. Can you take me to the Blaengarth Hospital to dry out? I'm going round the bend. Please. It's urgent.'

He was reeking of meths, a potential human fire-bomb. I had been visited by a number of such gentlemen but never by one demanding to be taken to a mental hospital as a matter of urgency. Eleanor was at a seminar in Newport. The children were out in the park with Marlene. Mrs Jenkins had gone home. Blaengarth was some fifteen miles away. I stood, speechless and paralysed by indecision.

'You're a man of the cloth,' his speech was slurred; 'supposed to be a Good Samaritan.'

That was a challenge I could not buck. 'Wait here,' I said. I went to my desk and wrote a hurried note: 'Have gone to Blaengarth Hospital. Explain later'. I placed it on the table in the kitchen and went back to the front door where my passenger was in a heap on the step.

'Get up!' I commanded, 'and let's go.'

He was very unsteady on his feet – so much so that I had to guide him to the back seat of my car. I locked the door for safety's sake. Then I got nervously into the front and made my way out on to the main road.

I had been to Blaengarth Hospital when I was at Pontywen, to visit a parishioner who was suffering from severe depression. This visit was going to be something entirely different. How different became apparent when I had driven about five miles towards our destination.

'Stop the car,' came a cry from the back, 'I want to get out.'

'Why do you want to get out?' I asked, with my foot on the accelerator rather than the brakes.

'I want to go back. I don't want to go there.'

'Now then, come off it,' I said. 'You have asked me to be the Good Samaritan and I am taking you where they can put you right. So if I were you I would be quiet and wait until we get to Blaengarth.'

By now he was tugging at the door handle of the back seat. 'You've locked this bloody door, you bugger. Let me out. I'm not going to that hell hole again. I had enough of that last time.' Then he tried to clamber over the seat to catch hold of me. Fortunately he was so uncoordinated that he fell back and subsided on to the seat behind me. For the next part of the journey he was sprawled comatose and incapable of any further physical effort.

'Thank God for the meths,' I said to myself and then apologised to the Almighty for commending the source of his misery.

Twenty minutes later, we drew up outside the gates of what had once been a workhouse at the turn of the century. My passenger was sitting upright, recognising his destination. A porter came out from the lodge. I turned down my window.

'I have a patient with me for your alcoholic unit,' I said.

'Straight ahead and turn left at the sign saying Ward F,' he instructed.

My passenger once again became extremely agitated. We drew up at the entrance of Ward F. I got out, locked my door and went into the ward. A short middle-aged man in a white coat came to meet me.

'What can I do for you, Reverend,' he enquired.

'I have someone who has been a patient here before. He arrived at my doorstep an hour or so ago and asked me to bring him here because he is suffering from DTs. I have never seen him before but he is reeking of meths and has been trying to get out of my car on my way here.'

The male nurse was softly spoken and somewhat effeminate. 'Don't worry, Vicar,' he reassured me.

He came out with me and looked inside the car. 'Oh! Victor,' he said. I unlocked the door. The nurse opened it. 'Come on in, old man. Let's see what we can do for you once again.'

'Victor' shrank away. 'I'm not going anywhere with that nancy boy. I'm going back.'

'Sorry, Victor, I'm afraid I'm not taking you back,' was my firm reply. 'You demanded to come here and this is where you stay.' My forehead was damp with sweat and my shirt was clinging to my body in a firm embrace.

Between us we managed to extricate Victor from the back seat and led him into the ward where he seemed to accept the inevitable. He collapsed into a chair in the Sister's office. I breathed a sigh of relief.

'I had better get back to my wife and family,' I said to the male nurse, as he saw me out of the ward. 'By the way, how often does he come here?'

'Victor is a regular customer, Reverend. He used to be a seaman until he hit the bottle. I don't know why he hangs about this part of the world. He comes from Liverpool. Anyway, thank you for bringing him here. I hope he doesn't trouble you any more, that's all.'

Eleanor came out of the front door as I pulled up in the drive. 'What on earth were you doing in Blaengarth Hospital?' she demanded. 'Did you feel a nervous breakdown coming on, or what? Your dinner has been ready for the last half an hour.'

'It was an emergency,' I replied. 'I had to rush a tramp called Victor there to dry out. He was suffering from a nasty bout of the DTs. He was on the doorstep begging me to take him to the hospital. It was a bit of a hair-raising journey because he decided he wanted to get out after we had gone a few miles.'

'If I were you, Frederick, I would have let him go and pester some other gullible cleric. Still, you have earned your brownie points for today.'

As we sat at table, I told her about Hugh's visit to Raglan House and how pleased he was with his 'digs'. 'The only fly in the ointment is the Thursday surgery of the peripatetic Mr Alabaster. Hugh does not want to have Thursday as his day off because he is dedicated to cricket and rugby on Saturdays. Apparently he is to have a trial with Abergelly Rugby Club in August. So that means, I am afraid, that he will have to come here every Thursday. I am sure we can feed one more mouth that day.'

'Can we indeed?' she retorted. 'Honestly, Secombe, you are the world's softest touch. Twice in the space of a couple of hours you have been taken for a ride, once by your new Curate and secondly both literally and metaphorically by a tramp. You know perfectly well that you will need assistance for weddings on a Saturday.'

'It's all right, dear,' I replied. 'I have told him that, once he is priested, he will have to take weddings.'

'I can see him now,' she said, 'with his cricket flannels underneath his cassock in the summer and his rugby outfit covered up in the winter. I bet they will be the quickest marriage services ever conducted in the parish church. The couples will be in and out before they realise they are married.'

The next morning I was doing my usual Saturday chore, reading through the collect epistle and gospel for the next day, Rogation Sunday. The opening words of the Gospel were taken from the sixteenth chapter of St John. 'Verily, verily I say unto you whatsoever you shall ask the Father in my name, he will give it you.' I always used the prayer book given to my grandfather by the Bishop of Hereford for being in the First Class at the Annual Examination held in the year 1875 by the Society for the Promotion of Christian knowledge, now known as SPCK. I put down the beautifully bound prayer book in its leather cover with the coat of arms of the Hereford diocese, and stared through the study window. I could see the allotment plots on the side of the hill just below the Brynfelin housing estate. In many rural parishes on Rogation Sunday, 'Asking Sunday', the congregation and parish priests would go into the fields for the blessing of the crops, a medieval tradition. 'Why not the blessing of the allotments,' I asked myself. 'If only I had thought of it earlier, I could have arranged some kind of religious ceremonial.' The more I thought of it the more eager I became to do it. Why wait until next year?

I left the prayer book on my desk and hurried down to the source of all knowledge, Tom Beynon. When I knocked at his door, he opened it and stood bewildered, pipe in hand. 'Vicar! Three visits in a matter of days. Nothing awful has happened I hope.'

'Not at all, Tom,' I replied. 'I've just had an idea and I would like to try it out tomorrow, if possible.'

'You had better come into the front room. The wife's cleaning the kitchen.' He led me into the parlour which was redolent of furniture polish. 'Sit down, Vicar,' he said, ushering me into a leather armchair beside the fireplace. He sat down opposite, puffing his pipeful of strong-smelling tobacco.

'Do you know who is the existing secretary of the Allotment Association which cultivates the land just below the Brynfelin estate,' I asked.

'Llew Hopkins,' he replied. 'Grows the biggest onions and leeks in Abergelly. Lives on the allotment when he's not working. He's an overman at the colliery. Excuse me asking, but why the hurry?'

'Tomorrow is Rogation Sunday, as you know. Well, it's the custom in country parishes for the Vicar and congregation to go out in the fields for the blessing of the crops. There aren't any fields around here but there are the allotments. I wondered if we could go there for the ceremony.'

'That's much too far away, Vicar,' he said. 'You don't need to go that distance. Just two streets away behind the Methodist Church there are a dozen small allotments. We could walk there from the church.'

'Wonderful,' I exclaimed.

'Hold on, Vicar,' he went on. 'What's the rush? Why not do this next year when there will be plenty of time to prepare for it. For example, you could never organise transport to the allotments at Brynfelin in a couple of hours. Not only that, but the congregation would want to have due notice.'

Now that I knew that there were allotments near at hand I was loth to postpone the event until next year. 'It's like this, Tom,' I said. 'I feel the congregation is in need of revitalisation now, not next year. This could be a surprise for them taking them out of the church building and into the world outside. I would preach a sermon on the need for God's blessing on our work, on our parish and even on the growing crops.'

He gave me a long look, as if he were deciding whether I had parted company with my sanity or whether I had made a valid point. 'Right,' he replied, 'if that's the way you feel, let's give it a go. They'll all be there this morning, doing their weekend stint of gardening. I'll just tell the missus that I'm off.'

A few minutes later he returned. 'I've told her what you've got in mind and she said she thinks it's lovely. So there's one satisfied customer.'

When we arrived at the patch of ground behind the Methodist Church we found it alive with furious activity. The amateur gardeners were watering, planting, weeding, putting up bean poles, or disappearing into the few glasshouses dotted about the place. Tom opened the gate and led me down to a little old man clad in an open-necked shirt with sleeves rolled and an ancient pair of trousers held up miraculously with braces, by one button at the back and two in the front. He wore a cloth cap which apparently had been a friend for many years. His attention was completely absorbed by two rows of lettuce which were competing with each other for space.

'Eli,' shouted Tom. 'This is the Vicar.'

Eli's head swivelled round. He peered at me through his metal-rimmed spectacles. 'Wot brings you down 'ere?' he enquired. 'If you're after a plot you've 'ad it. Just joking, of course.' He shook my hand. 'You're the first parson to come down 'ere, since I've been 'ere.' He pointed to the big Methodist Church. 'I've been on these allotments for the past forty-five years and none of those buggers 'ave been anywhere near, excuse the language.'

'Eli is the secretary of the allotment society,' said Tom. 'He has been that for many years.'

'How many years have you been secretary of the allotments?' shouted the warden.

'Thirty-six years and still going strong,' replied the old man. 'Wot do you want anyway, Vicar? You can 'ave some lettuce with pleasure.'

'Thank you,' I said. Then, raising my voice, I articulated very slowly, 'Would you like me to bless the allotments tomorrow morning after the service in church?'

He stared first at me and then at Tom. 'Wot did 'e say?' he asked him.

'The Vicar would like to come and say prayers here tomorrow morning. It's like the Harvest but this is to help the crops grow ready for the Harvest.'

Quite a few heads were turned in our direction as the warden was attempting to communicate with Eli.

'Well, I've 'eard everything now,' said Eli. 'Wot good is that going to do?'

'You'll have to wait and see,' bellowed Tom.

Half an hour later, when we had canvassed the other sons of the soil, it was obvious that they were one and all in favour of the idea. It was agreed that we should hold the ceremony at eleven o'clock the next morning. Three of the men indicated that they would turn up in church for the Communion Service. One of them said it would be the first time he had been at the altar since the last war.

'It's going to be a worthwhile effort,' commented Tom, 'if it's only to see Bill Jones at the altar rails. I remember him being confirmed in 1936 as a twelve-year-old. I doubt if he has had his Communion more than half a dozen times. His mother could never get him up in time for eight o'clock.

Perhaps if the service had been at half past nine, as it is now, he might have come more often.'

'Thanks, Tom, for all your help,' I said when we parted at the Vicarage gates. 'I think I had better get on with my sermon now.'

'If you don't mind me saying so,' he suggested, 'I think it would be advisable if you went to see Amos Perkins at his shop before you do anything else. You know what he's like about being consulted.'

'Informed, I think is the word,' I replied, 'since the event is a *fait accompli*. Anyway, I shall go down and tell him.'

When I went to his premises in the town centre, the assistant told me that he was over at the warehouse. I left a message asking him to ring me and made my way back to the Vicarage.

Eleanor had been out shopping when I had the rush of blood to my head. She was emptying the shopping basket on the kitchen table as I came into the room. 'I thought you would have been in the study preparing your few words for tomorrow,' she said.

'I was there until the Lord caused a light to shine upon the road to Damascus,' I replied. I told her about my sudden inspiration and the subsequent happenings.

'I hope he does not cause a cloudburst to descend upon the allotments at eleven o'clock tomorrow,' she remarked.

5

The Lord did not cause a cloudburst to descend upon the allotments. It was a glorious May morning, sunny and warm. However, there was a catastrophe which could not be blamed upon the Almighty. This was no act of God, the 'get out' for insurance companies. Human frailty was the cause and, I must admit, most of that frailty must be attributed to me. It all began in the vestry prior to the Family Communion Service as I was instructing the choir about the role they had to play in the procession to the Owen Street allotments. Under the regime of my predecessor they had been accustomed to singing the Litany during Morning Prayer on the first Sunday in the month.

'This morning,' I said, 'you will have to sing it as you walk. There will be no organ to support you but I am sure you will keep in tune.'

My words were rudely interrupted by the violent intrusion of Amos Perkins, purple in the face with anger. 'What is all this mumbo jumbo?' he demanded. 'I've only just heard of it when I came in. Why wasn't I informed? I am supposed to be your warden, the first person to be consulted when there is any innovation.'

'Didn't you get my message at your shop?' I asked. 'I told your assistant yesterday morning to get you to phone me when you came back from the warehouse. I heard nothing and I assumed you were otherwise engaged when you returned.' By now we had a very interested audience whose heads were turned towards each of the participants in the exchange, like spectators at a tennis match.

'I never had your message,' he shouted, 'and, if I had, I would have told you that I don't think this church should be involved in something which is more like a witchdoctor's ritual than a Christian ceremony.'

I exercised great restraint. 'Mr Perkins,' I said breathing heavily, 'the blessing of the crops is an ancient Christian ceremony which has been celebrated over hundreds of years and still is being carried out in many hundreds of parishes this morning. Whether you like it or not, after we all have made our Communion we shall proceed to the Owen Street allotments where I shall say prayers for God's blessing on the growing crops and then return to church for the final benediction. If you object to what is being done, then please stay in church until we come back. Now would you please go back into the nave and wait for the celebration of the holy mysteries to begin.' He glowered at me then closed the vestry door with a loud bang which must have startled the congregation. I turned to the choir who had been engrossed in the contretemps. 'Now, then shall we keep silence for a few moments before we enter into God's holy place and prepare ourselves to receive His blessed sacrament.' It was what could be described as a pregnant silence, suddenly broken by Herbert Evans, the eccentric bass who was expert at hymn numbers and interrupting sermons with loud yawns.

'I think he's right,' he growled. 'All this messing about with allotments. I tell you what, I'm not going out there in my cassock and surplice just to help that lot grow bigger carrots. I'll stay in church with Amos Perkins and I'll bet there'll be a lot more with him, believe me.' He looked around, his jaw jutting out more than usual. If he expected support it was not forthcoming. At least there would be but one dissentient left in the choirstalls. 'Now then,' I said, 'shall we compose ourselves once again? Let us pray.' The vestry prayer ended with a somewhat ragged 'Amen' and I went out to face the congregation with a big question mark in my mind and with a sinking feeling in my stomach.

When the choir had filed into their places, I asked everybody to be seated.

'Today,' I announced, 'is Rogation Sunday, Asking Sunday. Directly after we have made our Communion we shall go out of the church in procession, the choir leading the way, and proceed to the Owen Street allotments where I shall ask for God's blessing on the growing crops. As we go, we shall be singing the Litany which was originally intended to be sung in procession. This ceremony is many centuries old and can be traced back to the sixth-century Bishop Mamertus of Vienne in Southern France. Now then, shall we begin our service by singing the Rogation hymn 'To Thee Our God we fly, for mercy and for grace'.

It was a larger congregation than usual, amongst whom I noted Bertie Ellis, the local correspondent for the *South Wales Post*, who was making a note of all that I had been saying. Evidently word had got round.

As soon as I began my sermon, Herbert Evans emitted the loudest yawn I had heard from him since I came to St Peter's. I stopped speaking and focused my gaze on him. 'Mr Evans,' I said, 'I have only just begun my sermon. You have not had enough time to get bored. If you wish to go to sleep, I suggest you do it with your mouth closed. Otherwise

I must ask you to go to the vestry and put your feet up there. In any case I cannot possibly continue to preach God's word if I have to compete with your noises off. So please make your mind up. Either you leave us for the rest of the sermon or else you keep your mouth firmly shut.'

He stood up thrust his chin forward and pointed a finger at me. 'I'll leave you for the rest of the sermon all right – in fact I'll leave you for good.' He clambered over the legs of his fellow choristers, almost falling over in his haste to get out. He made his way down the aisle, muttering and glaring from side to side at the congregation as he did so. When he had slammed the vestry door shut, I tried to continue with my sermon. It was a fiasco. I could not concentrate on what I had to say, neither could the congregation. I remembered the advice given at my theological college. 'If you see that the congregation are not listening, shut up and come down from the pulpit. You are only wasting your time if you stay there.' I shut up and came down.

My heart was thumping and my hands were trembling when the service reached the administration of the sacrament. I found it difficult to hold the chalice steadily. It was only by the grace of God that I completed that part of the Eucharist without mishap. Now came the moment of truth when I announced that the choir would lead the way down the aisle and out through the west door to be followed by the congregation, walking in twos. Percy Wilkins, the burly youth who was the cross-bearer, came up to the sanctuary and took the processional cross out of its holder. 'O God the Father of heaven,' I began to intone in a wavering voice, 'have mercy upon us miserable sinners.' How many will stay in their pews, I wondered. Some were sitting and not standing. The whole of Amos Perkins' pew of followers, including Wot-you-Call Williams, were firmly glued to their seats. Eventually by the time we had arrived at the allotments it was apparent almost all of the worshippers were present for the ceremony. The choir had kept in tune throughout the Litany and I was feeling much less of a miserable sinner at the end than I was at the beginning.

Our procession had brought most of the inhabitants of Church Street and Evans Street to their doorsteps as we intoned our way past them and when we reached the allotments the amateur gardeners (including Old Eli), all of them dressed in their Sunday best, were there in force. The choir and congregation spread themselves out on the pathways, taking great care not to tread on the sacred soil which we had come to bless. I had just begun reading a prayer from Rogation tide, 'O Almighty God who hast created the earth for man', when my supplication was drowned by a loud shout from Eli.

'Get off those lettuces, you dull bugger!' I looked up to see a startled photographer who had positioned himself to take a picture of me leading the devotions. In his anxiety to get off Eli's lettuce he caught his foot against one of the stones which bordered the plot. The next second he was sprawled across the path dividing Eli's plot from his neighbour's, with his feet firmly planted in the middle of the old man's fragile seedlings, and with his face buried in a compost heap on the adjacent plot. Like a true professional he protected his apparatus by holding it close to his chest, which meant he was unable to get to his feet immediately without assistance. A number of volunteers came forward to help, causing further damage to the two allotment-holders' precious plants.

At this stage of the farcical proceedings my wife appeared on the scene to check that the fallen one had not suffered any serious injury. She seemed to be having trouble in keeping a straight face. After a cursory examination and an assurance from the photographer that he felt no pain, she came up to me and whispered, 'Next year, Secombe, I should stay inside, if I were you. It's less dangerous.'

When I resumed the Rogation prayers, I did so against a background of chattering which continued until I finished with the grace. The return to the church was more like a disorganised rabble than a dignified procession, with a certain amount of laughter involved. I wondered what I would find when we re-entered St Peter's. The building was empty, not a sight of Amos Perkins and his pew-full of camp followers. We were due to sing another hymn before the blessing. That was something I could not face. The sooner the service was over the better. 'If you will all kneel, we shall finish with the benediction,' I said. A few minutes later, we were back in the vestry where the choir gave vent to their feelings with a noisy discussion about the morning's exciting events. Ivor Hodges took me by the arm and led me to one side. 'Don't look so downcast, Vicar,' he said quietly. 'I know things did not go exactly smoothly but next year we can be more organised. It was a little bit precipitate today. There's one good thing to come out of it. You have put Herbert Evans in his place once and for all.'

'I have no desire to get rid of him,' I replied.

'You haven't got rid of him, Vicar. He'll be back, believe me, but he will be less inclined to indulge in his antics, I'm sure.'

'I hope so,' I said.

When Tom Beynon came into the vestry to count the collection, he was equally reassuring. 'I had a word with Eli after the service at the allotments,' he said. 'Of course he was annoyed at that photographer, but, as he told me, he knows that had nothing to do with you or your idea of blessing the earth and its plants. I'm positive he will like to keep the custom going. By next year we will be better prepared.'

'That's what Ivor Hodges said,' I replied.

They were not the sentiments expressed by Amos Perkins after Evensong later that day. 'I've heard what happened at the allotments,' he crowed. 'What a laughing stock we are going to be! I hope you have learned your lesson, young man. It's one thing to have big ideas and you've got plenty of those. It's quite another thing to carry them out.' The words 'young man' stung me more than the rest of his insulting remarks.

'My title, Mr Perkins, is Vicar, not "young man".'

'Well, Vicar,' he replied, loading the word with as much venom as he could put into it, 'if you lived up to that title you would not have humiliated Herbert Evans as you did from the pulpit. You have driven a man out of the church who has been attending St Peter's since he was a baby in his mother's arms, and that is a long time before you were born.'

I was visited by a most unChristian impulse to inflict violence upon his person. It was not a still small voice which prevented me but the sound of Tom Beynon's voice as he entered the vestry. He was singing the closing hymn of the service, 'Love Divine, all loves excelling.'

'I'll see you both at the PCC on Tuesday,' Amos snapped and left us.

'What was all that about?' enquired Tom. 'He was in a hurry, wasn't he? If you don't mind me saying so, Vicar, you look as if you've had all the colour drained from your face. Trouble again?'

'You could say that,' I replied.

'Don't you think', Eleanor said when I recounted the contretemps in the vestry later that evening, 'that you should put a brake on your many-sided attempts to make a big impression in Abergelly? First of all you said that before all else it was necessary to put the church and the church hall in a good state of repair. Now you are about to organise a team to put up a pre-fab church on the Brynfelin estate and a campaign to make the congregation dig much deeper into their pockets, not to mention side issues like the invasion of allotments or courting the aristocracy to subsidise the masonry work on your concrete jungle. You are like an ammunition dump hit by a shell and exploding in several directions at one and the same time. Take some advice from your favourite doctor. Go easy, Vicar. I hate to sound like Amos Perkins, but if you try to do the impossible you are going to end up with a nervous breakdown.'

Next morning I spent a lot of time on my knees in church after I had finished Matins, not in pious meditation but in a contemplation of my life from my student days until my arrival in Abergelly. My wife was painfully accurate in describing me as an exploding ammunition dump. At college I was President of the Students Union, editor of the college magazine, President of the Debating Society, a member of the Dramatic Society, the comedian in the college concert party and, in the little time left, studying for an honours degree in history. It was small wonder that my history professor suggested that I should get my priorities right. At Pontywen, I was engaged in redecorating the church, organising door-to-door visiting and running the Gilbert and Sullivan Society – not only directing it but taking the leading tenor role. Now I was about to become the Pooh-Bah par excellence, destroying myself in the process.

Like the prodigal son, I came to myself and realised what an idiot I was. By the time I had left the church I had made up my mind that I would take one step at a time. At the Parochial Church Council meeting I would suggest that we spend a few months repairing the church hall and then decorating the church. We would appoint two committees, one to revitalise giving in the parish and the other to prepare for the erection of the prefabricated church at the end of the year. That in itself was a very demanding programme but at least it was organised and practicable, I told myself. Now I had to convince the PCC that this was so, an entirely different proposition.

As I returned to the Vicarage, I had a pang of conscience when I remembered that today was the opening of Eleanor's surgery on the estate. I had promised that I would come and bless the premises before she began her work there and I had not thought to say a prayer for her new venture but consoled myself with the knowledge that I would be saying prayers at the surgery later that morning. There was an air of great excitement in the Vicarage. Eleanor had contacted the local newspaper who had printed a few paragraphs under the heading 'NEW SURGERY FOR BRYNFELIN'. The chairman of the health authority had promised to attend the opening ceremony with other members of the committee and a few councillors. Using the money from the sale of her practice in Pontywen, my wife had invested in the latest equipment available. 'After being without a doctor on the spot for so long, the people on the estate deserve the very best that money can supply,' she had said. The three-bedroomed house had been converted into a medical centre. Downstairs, the parlour became the waiting room. A counter was erected beside the stairs and became the reception desk behind which was the kitchen. Upstairs was the surgery, occupying the biggest of the bedrooms, next to which was the dispensary. The third room was a store room. Eleanor was hoping that perhaps one day it would provide a surgery for a partner, should the workload become too heavy for a single-handed practice.

Marlene was having great difficulty trying to control David who had been promised that he could come to the grand opening. He darted away from her when I came though the door and attacked my cassock, shouting, 'Mummy did say that I could have a try at her telescope to listen, didn't she, Dad? Marlene said she didn't. She did, didn't she?'

'Marlene is just teasing you. Now you start behaving yourself, otherwise we shall leave you here with Elspeth.'

This had an instant effect. He had no desire to be abandoned in the Vicarage with his baby sister when there was so much excitement to be had in the new surgery. There was a delicious smell of baking coming from the kitchen where Mrs Jenkins was making her Welsh Cakes.

Betty Thomas, the newly appointed receptionist, was helping Eleanor to prepare sandwiches for the medical beanfeast. She was a plump, rosy-cheeked, blue-eyed young lady in her early twenties with an engaging smile. It was easy to see why my wife had chosen her from the list of applicants. She was so different from the dragon she had inherited from her predecessor in the Pontywen Surgery whose countenance was more appropriate to a prison wardress. By the time she had barked the name of the next patient that poor soul entered the consulting room with an inferiority complex which added a further complication to the diagnosis confronting the doctor. Furthermore, Betty had a CV which revealed a Higher Certificate in Maths, Physics and Chemistry. Had she achieved distinctions in those subjects, she would have been eligible for a good scholarship to a university with a medical school. Her one desire was to be a doctor. Since her parents were working-class and blessed with a large family, such an aspiration was something of a dream. As a receptionist to a doctor at least she could sit behind a receptionist's desk in a surgery and be in close contact with her dream.

The opening ceremony was due to take place at two-thirty p.m. Eleanor had discovered that the favourite tipple of the chairman of the Health Committee was brandy with ginger ale. Accordingly she had an ample supply of both and a crate of champagne, together with a crate of beer for the proletariat. Surgery times had been fixed at four-thirty p.m. to six p.m. and nine a.m. to ten-thirty a.m. 'Two hours is ample to clear the surgery before the influx of patients.'

She had miscalculated. At four-thirty p.m. there was a large queue of patients outside the surgery. Inside, the Health Committee showed no signs of an imminent departure. Indeed they gave every indication that the party had yet to get into full swing. Eleanor looked at the clock she had installed in the consulting room. Councillor Joe Davies, the chairman of the Health Committee, was being served with his fifth glass of brandy and ginger ale by Betty Thomas who was looking desperate.

'I am sorry to have to put an end to our festivities,' announced my wife, 'but it is time for play to end and work to begin. It has been a great joy to have such a wonderful send-off and now I hope you all will not be offended if I send you off. Thank you for your tremendous support and may all the people of Brynfelin continue to have the same support that you have given me.'

Councillor Joe Davies swallowed his glass of good cheer in one gulp.

'On behalf of the 'ealth Committee, I should like to thank Dr Secombe for 'er 'ospitality on such an h'auspicious occasion. I am sure that with the blessing which 'er 'usband has bestowed upon this – er – h'auspicious enterprise, she will go from strength to strength, thanks to the – er – 'elp given 'er by our wonderful Aneurin Bevan.' He made it sound as if the former Health Minister had contributed personally to the setting up of the surgery. 'You know,' he went on, 'if it wasn't for 'im, you would all be paying for the doctor. Now you get as good a treatment as the nobs and for nothing. I remember when I was a kid . . .'

My wife's patience, which was never one of her strong points, snapped. 'Thank you for your kind remarks, Councillor Davies,' she said, 'and now to work.'

The chairman of the Health Committee glowered at Eleanor in drunken resentment, evidently peeved at this surgical operation on his oration. Betty Thomas poured him his

85

sixth glass of brandy and ginger ale to soothe the pain and then indulged in a quick cleaning up of the festive debris. A few minutes later I escorted Councillor Davies to the back door with the help of the secretary to the Health Committee who had ferried him to the occasion.

I was driving back to the Vicarage with David babbling in the back seat about having a go at the telescope. 'I could hear Mummy's tummy, Dad.' How she had managed to escape from the mêlée to give him 'a go at the telescope' was a mystery which my wife could explain later. By the size of the queue of patients it would appear that the explanation would be considerably later. Marlene, who had been looking after Elspeth, met me at the door when I came in.

'Mr Featherstone has been on the phone. He wants to speak with you urgently. I have written his phone number on the pad. The other thing, Vicar, is that Elspeth has been sick twice. I've put her to bed but she has quite a temperature and she's got a lot of pain in her stomach.'

'Talk about trouble at the mill,' I said to myself, 'it's nothing like trouble at the Vicarage.' I dialled the Featherstone number so hastily that it took me two false calls before I contacted our benefactor.

'Ah, Vicar,' he sighed, 'at last. I tried three times before I got an answer and then the fourth time to find you were out.'

'I'm afraid our nursemaid was upstairs with our younger child who is ill,' I replied.

'Sorry about that; I hope she is better soon,' he replied. 'Anyway I am afraid that there has been a change in the situation as far as the temporary buildings here are concerned, the board of directors has decided that, in view of our increased production as a result of our recent extension, they need the space occupied by our temporary wooden buildings for an enlarged transport facility. They want the buildings removed within the next fortnight. I know that I told you that you could wait as long as you like before putting up your new church. Perhaps you can find somewhere to store the buildings before you re-erect them into their new form.'

There was a long pause while my mind struggled to come to terms with the urgency.

'Are you there?' he said.

'Yes, Mr Featherstone,' I replied.

'I am sorry about this,' he added apologetically. 'I had thought that I could keep them here until you were ready. This is the price of progress, I am afraid.'

'Don't worry. I shall find some means of keeping them safe until we are ready for their resurrection. I am not one to look a gift horse in the mouth.'

When I put the phone down I realised that I had not the faintest idea of how to protect the gift horse. The Brynfelin estate housed many predators who were capable of dismembering it. A twenty-four-hour watch was the only answer. To organise such a task on a voluntary basis would tax the ability of a superman let alone that of a Vicar or church-warden. As I sat at my desk I could hear Elspeth upstairs crying in pain. It was one of those moments in my life when I felt like a pygmy in the grip of the Giant Despair. I went up to the little girl's bedroom where Marlene was trying to comfort her. The child was obviously in great distress. I picked her up and cuddled her to no avail. I ran downstairs to phone the surgery. Betty Thomas answered the phone.

'Vicar,' she said, 'we're up to our eyes in it at the moment.'

'I'm sorry, Betty,' I replied. 'I know how busy you must be but I must speak to my wife. Elspeth is in terrible pain.'

Eleanor was at the other end in seconds. I told her about the sickness, the high temperature and the pain.

'I'll be down straight away,' she said.

I went back upstairs to our daughter. As I did so, I remembered what had happened to my four-year-old sister who had died of peritonitis after our doctor had misdiagnosed appendicitis as indigestion. As I held the child in my arms, she was now screaming in agony. The seconds ticked by like minutes in my wait for the arrival of my wife. When the front door burst open and she came bounding up the stairs, I had never known such tremendous relief. She burst into the room and took Elspeth from my arms. She had her stethoscope with her and in no time she was examining her midriff.

'Hold her while I phone for an ambulance,' she ordered. 'She has acute appendicitis.'

Shivers ran up and down my spine as my wife went down the stairs two at a time to call for the ambulance. All the while Elspeth was crying pitifully. I rocked her in my arms and tried to sing. 'Baby, baby, bunting,' her favourite nursery rhyme. It was a waste of breath. The louder I sang, the louder she cried.

'You can give her to me now,' said my wife as she came back to the bedroom. 'The ambulance should be here in a few minutes. The sooner she is operated on the better.'

Half an hour later we were in Abergelly Hospital, a much larger place than its Pontywen counterpart and much more modern, some of it built during the war to accommodate the casualties. Our daughter was rushed into the operating theatre as soon as we arrived in the ambulance. As we waited outside, Eleanor caught hold of my hand. 'Don't worry, love,' she said. 'I am sure we have caught it in time and Roger Williams is a brilliant surgeon, one of the best in South Wales.'

I have never known the hands of the clock to crawl around the dial so slowly. An hour went by. It seemed an eternity. Then the doors of the theatre opened and Roger Williams came up to us, whipping off his mask to reveal a broad smile.

'Your worries are over,' he proclaimed. 'We have taken out her appendix, in the nick of time. That is one part of her body which won't trouble her any more.'

I went back to the Vicarage leaving my wife to sit by Elspeth's bedside until she woke up and needed maternal comfort. Back home, David wanted to know how his little sister was faring and why he could not have put the 'telescope' on her tummy to find out what was wrong. Marlene burst into tears of relief. She loved our little girl deeply and had been desperately worried about her sudden illness in the absence of her mother.

'Now then, David,' I said, 'off to bed.'

'Come and read me a story, please, Dad,' he replied.

'Marlene will read you one, won't you?' She nodded her head and blew her nose at the same time. 'Daddy has a lot of work to do tonight.' I kissed him and patted his bottom as I turned him towards the door. Our nursemaid lifted him up and gave him a fireman's lift over her shoulder. She was a burly girl.

Left alone in the study, my thoughts turned to the problem of the 'pre-fab' church on the Brynfelin estate. If only that could be eliminated as quickly as Elspeth's appendicitis. Perhaps an all-out effort could be made immediately to prepare the site and I could plead with Bernard Featherstone for a week's extension of the deadline. That would give me three weeks to have everything ready for the erection of the building. It was too late to contact our works foreman; he would be busy serving fish and chips to the populace of Abergelly. Another visit to Tom Beynon was the only alternative.

When I knocked on his door for the second time in less than a week, I felt a sense of guilt. If I keep on plaguing him like this, I said to myself, he will wish he was at work for sixteen hours a day and free from the attentions of the new Vicar. He opened the door and, when he saw me, said 'This is for the second time of asking,' as if he were reading the bans of marriage. Puffing his foul smelling pipe, he led me into the kitchen. 'The wife's out at her sister's,' he said, 'so I am now enjoying my third pipeful of tobacco. Well, if you can stand the fumes, Vicar, sit down and have a glass of stout.' As he poured out my drink he murmured. 'I must say you look as if you need something stronger.'

'No, it's all right, Tom,' I replied. 'I'm afraid I've had a very trying time during the past couple of hours. Little Elspeth has been rushed into hospital with appendicitis. She has had the operation and all is well. Eleanor's at her bedside waiting for her to wake up.'

'Thank God, everything is OK Vicar.'

'The other thing is that Mr Featherstone, the man who is giving us the temporary church at Brynfelin, has phoned to say that the board of directors insist that the sheds must be delivered within the next fortnight. How on earth are we going to keep them in safe custody ready for the building?'

He was silent for a minute. 'There's only one answer,' he said, 'and that is that we get down to work straight away.'

6

The next morning I awoke with an acute pain in my stomach. Eleanor was still asleep. The rising-ritual involved me as the tea maker. When I pulled back the bedclothes as gently as I could to avoid disturbing my wife, the pain intensified. By the time I was putting on my slippers it had become excruciating. Had appendicitis been a contagious condition I would have been convinced I had caught it from Elspeth. No longer able to contain myself, I yelped with the pain. Eleanor sat up suddenly. 'What on earth is the matter with you?' she said sharply.

'I've got a terrible pain in my stomach,' I replied.

'Oh, no!' she exclaimed. 'First Elspeth, now you. Open your pyjama jacket and show me where this pain is.' She felt my stomach and my abdomen. 'Lie back on the bed,' she ordered, 'and I'll get my stethoscope.'

A few minutes later she was back with her 'telescope' draped around her dressing gown. She listened to most of my anatomy, asking me to pinpoint the source of my trouble. As she finished her examination, she said, 'Don't worry, love, there is nothing seriously wrong with you. It's the result of all the tension you have had since you came to Abergelly. Evidently you have inherited your father's trouble – nervous indigestion. I'll get you some tablets which will ease the pain. I think it is about time that the Lord stopped treating us like Job.'

My father had suffered from dyspepsia ever since I could remember. When I was a boy I had to take the doctor's prescription to the chemist to pick up a packet of powder prepared in the back room and tied up with string. He used to tell us children, 'That's come from the White Cliffs of Dover to make me better.' He was an incurable romantic. The remedy for his stomach trouble could not have originated from anything so mundane as a chemist shop.

Later that morning, when the pain had abated, I telephoned Jack Richards to impart the information about the sudden change in the building programme.

'Well, Vicar,' he said, 'there should not be much trouble in preparing the site. It is pretty level. We'll have to prepare a trench for drainage and sewerage. At the moment I don't know the dimensions etcetera. If I could see these office buildings, I could work out what is needed.'

'I'll get in touch with Mr Featherstone right away,' I replied, 'and ring you back.' Mr Featherstone was engaged but his secretary promised to get him to phone me when he was free. Evidently it must have been an important conversation because I heard nothing until an hour later.

'Sorry to keep you waiting,' said our benefactor, 'but it was a lucrative call and I have clinched a very good deal.' He sounded happy. 'Now what can I do for you?'

I told him that our 'works foreman' needed to have a look at the future church.

'As soon as possible,' he replied. 'This afternoon, if he likes. We need the space badly since our trade is booming.'

Jack Richards was busy preparing for his lunchtime customers when I rang back. 'Be up here at three o'clock, Vicar, and I'll be ready.'

Eleanor came in as I put the phone down. 'I have been in to see Elspeth after I finished morning surgery. She's fine and she wants to see her daddy. How is that stomach?'

'Fine,' I replied. 'Jack Richards thinks we could have everything ready in a fortnight and we're going down to Cardiff to measure up the buildings this afternoon.'

'*We* are going to measure the buildings. Come off it, Fred. You mean *he* is going to do that. You couldn't measure the size of a tea chest let alone a complex of huts. Anyhow, please see your little daughter first. They are very pleased with her. Therefore she should be home before very long. By the way, the surgery was packed this morning. I shall need help, I can tell you.'

When lunch was over I went to the hospital to see my little daughter who was sitting up with her teddy bear on one side of her and her 'mama' doll on the other side. After carrying on a conversation with the three of them, I made my way to the fish 'bar' to pick up Jack Richards. He was standing outside his shop, arrayed in his best suit. Evidently his wardrobe was odour-proof since there was not the faintest aroma of frying-fat when he joined me in the front seat of my car. 'I went to see Tom Beynon last night', I told him, 'and he has said that he will contact as many members as possible to help prepare the site.'

'We'll need as many as we can get, and they must be workers, not passengers. Tom will know that in any case. If we can get the building up in the next three weeks or so it should be ready for opening in about three months' time. There's the plumbing to do, the electrics, the carpentry, the painting. Thank God it's summertime with the long evenings. Have you thought about what's to go inside, Vicar?

They've closed Bethesda Chapel and are talking about selling it. I bet you could have the pews from in there for a song.'

By the time the belching chimney stacks of the Featherstone Engineering Company came into sight, my head was spinning. I stopped the car at the entrance to the works. An attendant came out of his cubby hole and enquired somewhat officiously about our business. On hearing we had an appointment with the boss he became obsequious and raised the bar to give us entry, after giving us detailed directions of the route to head office. It was a pre-war red-brick building, with a recently constructed concrete extension adjoining it. Both buildings were suffering from the effects of industrial grime, part of the price paid for profit.

We waited a few minutes in the reception room before a secretary ushered us into the chairman's office. Bernard Featherstone came to greet us, shaking our hands warmly and inviting us to take a seat on the two chairs waiting for us.

'So you are in charge of the building of the church, Mr Richards,' he said. 'Obviously you are in the building trade.'

'I was once,' replied Jack, 'but now I keep a fish and chip shop.' The chairman's eyebrows moved upwards. 'My father was a builder and so was I,' he went on, 'until I had to give it up because of my health. When the Vicar came to see me to ask whether I would be in charge of putting up this new church, I jumped at it like a shot. It will be like the old days. Once a builder always a builder. I tell you what, I'd rather be dealing with bricks and mortar than with fish and chips any day.'

Jack was all set for a lengthy monologue when the phone rang. 'Saved by the bell,' I said to myself.

'Would you tell him to ring back in about ten minutes' time?' instructed Mr Featherstone. He put down the receiver and then pointed to his desk. 'I have all the plans and details of the offices here for you, Mr Richards. I am sorry I can't come with you to show the buildings but I shall ask my secretary to get someone to take you around them. In the meanwhile would you both care for a small dram before your inspection?'

Some ten minutes later one of the clerks was escorting us to the empty sheds of the temporary offices. One of these was sufficiently large enough to act as the main body of the church. Jack measured windows and doors, wall heights etc., quite unnecessarily, I thought, since he had all the details in his hands. However, it seemed to impress the clerk who must have imagined that the fish and chip retailer was a master builder.

On our way back to Abergelly he continued with his monologue which had been interrupted by the hour at the steelworks. He had reached the story of his first assignment as a builder at the age of twenty-five when we arrived outside Cardiff. When we pulled up outside his shop his career had not yet been ended in the construction industry. 'I must tell you more some other time,' he said.

'You must do that,' I replied and opened the door for him to get out.

'I enjoyed our chat,' were his parting words. I was about to say that the pleasure was mutual but my conscience would not allow it.

'See you soon,' I answered through the opened window and then put my foot on the accelerator to make good my escape.

It was providential that he did not believe in committees, I told myself. 'All committees do is talk,' he had said when I met him first.

We had just finished our evening meal a few hours later when there was a ring on the doorbell. Since we had both been to the hospital to visit our daughter, dinner was at eight-thirty instead of seven-thirty. Our conversation over our food had been a constant battle with the noise of the Friday evening bell ringers' practice. The bell tower was only a few yards away from the Vicarage and, since it contained eight bells, the competition was heavily weighted in favour of the ringers.

'What now!' exclaimed my wife. 'Who could be so inconsiderate as to call at this time of the night?'

I opened the front door to discover Bill Bailey, the Captain of the ringers. My wife and I had Christened him, 'Won't you come home?' a title derived from the old musical hall song. He was a tall, thin man with a large, untidy moustache disfiguring his upper lip. A surly individual whose sole interest was in campanology, he was a constant irritant since he never appeared to be present in church once the bells had ceased to ring, like most of his team. The only member of his company who never missed a service and who also sang in the choir was Ivor Hodges, the headmaster of the Bryntirion Secondary School. He had told me that he had words with Bill to no avail.

'Sorry to disturb you, Vicar,' he said, 'but I would like to have your permission for a team from the Gloucester diocese to ring our bells.'

'You had better come in, Mr Bailey,' I replied, feeling in the mood to cross swords with him. We went into the study and I ushered him into a seat at some distance from my desk to indicate that the interview was not to be a cosy *tête-à-tête*.

'Before you give me details about the occupation of our bell tower by the Gloucester ringers, I should like to have a few words about your attendance in church as opposed to your attendance in the bell tower. The purpose of bell ringing is to summon a congregation to worship. It is not an end in itself.'

He frowned and began to nibble the ends of his drooping moustache.

'I know I have not been long in the parish but since I have been here I cannot recall a single occasion when I have seen you or some of your team at the altar rails or amongst the congregation. Quite frankly I don't know how you have the nerve to call people to a service and then walk away before it begins. I expect you are a regular attendant at meetings of the Diocesan Bell Ringers' Association. It's about time you gave the same attention to your parish church.'

By now his moustache had been nibbled to such an extent that the droop had disappeared as he stroked it upwards. There was a silence as he struggled to find words for his reply. Evidently he was more than sorry that the Gloucester ringers had requested permission to ring the bells of Abergelly Parish Church.

'Well, Vicar,' he began, 'the old Vicar didn't mind us ringing the bells and then going home. As long as the bells were rung that's all that he wanted. I keep pigeons myself and spend my Sunday morning seeing to them. So does Les Jones; he's got a loft further down the street where I live. Then we and some of the other ringers meet in the Workingmen's Club for a drink at dinner time. That's our routine. If you want that to end, then you'd better find another team of ringers.' He pulled an envelope out of his pocket. 'There's the letter from Gloucester; you can answer it yourself. Goodnight!' He was up on his feet and out through the door before I could say another word.

'Who was that?' asked my wife when I came back to the dining room.

'Won't you come home?' I replied, 'and I'm afraid he won't come to ring the bells any more and neither will all his cronies.'

'The children will be glad about that on Friday nights,' she commented, 'and so will Marlene. No more disturbed sleep. More to the point, what will the parish say? They have been listening to those bells for donkeys' years. My dear Fred, for a new broom you are doing an awful lot of sweeping. What brought this on?'

I told her about my onslaught on him and his reaction. 'You were hardly diplomatic, were you?' she said. 'Still, I admire you for the stand that you took. So the bells will remain silent.'

'Not quite,' I replied. 'There is one bell that will not be stilled.'

'What do you mean?' she asked.

'Ivor Hodges is a bell ringer,' I said, 'and apparently he had spoken to Bill and his cohorts about their non-attendance in church, only to be put in his place. So there will be a call to worship on Sunday even if it is a solo effort. What's more, why shouldn't he be put in charge of the tower and train his own band of ringers? At least he would see that it would be a condition of their ringing that they should be present at worship.'

The next morning I was knocking on the door of Ivor Hodges at Number 13, Beaufort Crescent, a detached house in the prosperous area of Abergelly. He appeared in a sleeveless open-necked shirt and flannels.

'Come on in, Vicar,' he said. 'You have just caught me before I go down to the school sports field to watch our cricket team play their deadly rivals from Abergelly Grammar School. It's going to be a needlematch since both sides are unbeaten so far this season. You must come down one day and see them play. One or two of the youngsters have quite a future ahead of them.'

A few minutes later we were sitting down in his front room, overlooking an immaculately trimmed lawn and enjoying a cup of coffee supplied by Mair, his wife, an elegant lady who apologised for her appearance in a housecoat which could have been mistaken for an attractive dress. Evidently the Lord had smiled graciously upon the Hodges household and blessed them abundantly.

'I shan't keep you long, Ivor,' I said. 'How would you like to be Captain of the Abergelly Parish Church bell ringers?'

'Explain yourself, please, dear Vicar,' he replied.

'Last night I had a contretemps with William Bailey in the course of which I had made it plain that I expected those who had rung the bells to raise their voices in worship afterwards. According to Bill, the postscript to bell ringing was a couple of hours in the pigeon loft followed by a noggin with the other bell ringers in the Workingmen's Club. He saw no reason to change what he called the ringers' "routine" and left in high dudgeon, leaving me with a letter from a bell tower somewhere in Gloucestershire requesting permission to ring our bells. That's it in a nutshell,' I said.

'And very concisely and effectively put, if I may say so,' added the headmaster.

'So I wait for your answer after due consideration of all that is involved. Take your time, whether it is a week or a month, but be assured that the former things are passed away most definitely. In the meanwhile could you please ring one bell to call the faithful to worship?'

'In answer to the last question, of course I will,' he replied. 'In answer to your first question I may not need a month to give you an answer but I shall certainly need a fair amount of time. First of all, I am a busy man and teaching novices how to ring a bell is not an easy task. It will require time and patience. Secondly, I have been a mate of all those who have been with me in the tower and I have no wish to be spurned by them as a blackleg. If I accept your offer, I shall feel that first of all I shall have to contact each one of them and ask them if they would be prepared to come back on your terms, even including Bill Bailey. Should they refuse, as I expect they will, then I shall accept your invitation to become master in the bell tower and to do all I can to recruit volunteers.'

'Fair enough,' I said. 'By the way, would you mind if I came down to watch the match for a short while? I can't stay long because I have a wedding.'

'It will be a pleasure to have your company, Vicar,' Ivor replied. 'You will be able to see for yourself that I was not exaggerating the talents of those young lads, one or two of them as young as thirteen.'

The school sports field was situated in a valley and surrounded by a cordon of trees. A wooden pavilion, boasting a verandah, overlooked a superbly maintained cricket ground with two large sight screens at each end. When we arrived, the boys, clad in flannels and shirts which appeared to have been the objects of motherly attention, were practising at the nets and on the field. It was a sunny morning and the relaxed atmosphere prior to the 'needlematch' was the perfect antidote for my nervous indigestion which had flared up once again after my confrontation with the bell ringer. As I sat in a deckchair alongside the headmaster and clapped the opening batsmen on their way out to the middle, I felt at peace with the world. Soon the two young fifteen-year-olds were knocking the older grammar-school bowling in a spate of run making.

My enjoyment was cut short by the sight of my wife's car appearing through the gates of the field.

'Trouble!' I exclaimed and fell out of the deckchair in my haste to get up.

'What on earth is the matter?' asked Ivor Hodges in astonishment.'

'I'll soon know,' I replied. 'My wife has just arrived at high speed.'

I picked myself up and hurried down the steps of the pavilion to meet her as she ran across the path.

'Where's the fire?' I said.

'It's not a fire, Frederick. It's hot water and you're in it, right up to your neck. A bride and groom are waiting for you at the church together with half the population of Abergelly by the look of it. It's a good thing Mrs Hodges was in and able to tell me where you were.'

I looked at my watch. It was ten past twelve. The wedding was booked for twelve o'clock. As we ran towards her car, the few spectators ignored the cricket and watched the race to see who would get there first. It was no contest. Eleanor was at the wheel and revving the engine before I got to the car.

'If you keep on doing things like this, it will be a heart attack you will be likely to have, not nervous indigestion,' she warned.

'I didn't realise it was this time,' I said.

'Everybody else did, except you, apparently,' came the reply.

She pulled up at the back of the church with a screech of brakes and I dashed into the vestry. Fortunately I had filled in the registers which were ready on the desk. Evan Roberts the organist was coming to the end of his repertoire, by the sound of it. His playing of Jeremiah Clarke's trumpet voluntary had more than his usual quota of uncertain notes. From the noise emanating from the nave it was obvious that the natives were restless. I thrust my head through my surplice and found difficulty getting my arms through the sleeves in my panic. My stole was suspended around my neck with one side almost on the floor and the other around my midriff. I grabbed hold of my prayer book and hurried out into the nave to be confronted with a hostile silence, ending the tumult which had preceded it. There was no sign of the bridegroom and the best man in the front pew. My wife was right. I was in hot water, right up to my neck. With a sickly smile, in a vain attempt to placate the congregation I moved quickly down the aisle to the west end of the church where I found the bridegroom and the best man in earnest conversation with the bride, her mother and her father.

'You've spoilt her day,' snapped the mother.

It was the beginning of one of the most disastrous

marriage services I have ever conducted. I led the bride-groom, and his best man down to their pew. The future husband was pale and trembling.

'Come on, Mick, pull yourself together.' exhorted his friend.

'I should sit there and compose yourself for a minute,' I added. 'When you hear the 'Wedding March' being played come out and stand here at the chancel step.'

I made my way back to the west door. The bride was in tears and the badly applied mascara was blackening her countenance. An irate mother produced a handkerchief from her handbag and proceeded to smear the eyelash adornment over the bridal cheeks, giving the impression that the poor girl had just come to the surface after a shift in the mines.

'Now, look what you've done!' shouted the matriarch at me. Joe Williams, the verger was standing by the hymn books, an interested spectator.

'Go down to the vestry and get a flannel and towel,' I ordered.

A bewildered assembly of wedding guests and onlookers watched his big bulk lumbering down the aisle and into the vestry, reappearing with a wet flannel and towel. By now, all heads were turned towards the west door. In the church porch the cleansing operation was under way.

'Go and ask your Auntie Elsie if she's got her powder compact with her,' said the bride's mother to her youngest daughter who was the only bridesmaid. In no time at all she was back, breathless, with the powder compact.

When the bride looked at herself in the mirror, she shrieked. 'Oh, my God!'

Before she could indulge in any more blasphemy, her

mother instructed, 'Put that powder puff in there and give yourself a good dose of it. Go on!' She was a very forceful lady. When the treatment was complete, she kissed her daughter on the cheek and marched into the church to the front pew on the bride's side, leaving a faint red mark on an otherwise clean face.

The bride's father, looking uncomfortable in a new suit more than likely purchased on the 'never-never', turned to me and said, 'Do you think we can start now, Vicar? I'm dying for a pint.'

'Dad!' remonstrated his daughter.

I went to the opened west door and signalled to the organist, whose fingers had long ceased wandering over the noisy keys, that the time had come at last to herald the entry of the bride. He launched into Wagner's opus with such vigour and at such a pace that the procession could have galloped down the aisle. Meanwhile I could see the best man hauling the bridegroom out of his front seat as we made our way to the chancel. It was fortunate for the bridegroom that he had a burly friend to support him. It looked to me as if he was on the verge of collapse.

I announced the first hymn, 'Love divine', to a congregation who preferred talking to singing. Considering that there must have been at least 100 in the church, the only voices heard in praise were those of myself, the organist and a lady on the bride's side who fancied herself as a soprano soloist. When the hymn ended, I took the hymnbook which the bride and groom were sharing, or rather that she was holding and that he was pretending to hold in his trembling hand.

'Dearly beloved, we are gathered together here in the sight of God and of this congregation to join together this man and this woman in the holy estate of matrimony,' I began and got no further. The bridegroom's knees buckled and he collapsed into the arms of his best man, as his bride gazed down upon him in dismay.

Michael John Buckley was barely five foot tall and an anaemic specimen of manhood. He was laid out full-length in the front pew while I hurried into the vestry to get a glass of water. When I came back, he was sitting up surrounded by relatives and, by the glazed look in his eyes, uncertain of his whereabouts.

'Here we are, Mick,' I said, 'take a sip of this water.' I held the glass and put it to his mouth. He took a sip and then shook his head, as if trying to bring himself out of his stupor. Gradually his eyes focused on me.

'I'm sorry, Vicar,' he murmured, 'but I must have passed out.'

'You certainly did,' I replied. 'Just stay where you are for a few moments and, when you feel fit enough, we shall carry on with the service.'

In the meanwhile the bride had completely ignored the inert figure of her future husband and had turned to her mother for comfort after another episode had 'spoiled her day'. Once again Auntie Elsie's powder compact had to come into use, this time in the privacy of the vestry. It must have been five minutes before the service was resumed. I copied the organist's pace as I sped through the pages of the Book of Common Prayer, since the pallor of the bride-groom's face suggested that it was not impossible that he might do an encore before the ceremony was ended. When we moved into the vestry after the blessing, I gave a silent prayer of thanks to the Almighty that there had been no further mishap.

It was a premature prayer. As the parents, bride and groom plus best man and bridesmaid crowded into the small clergy vestry, they were followed by the photographer.

'Excuse me,' I said, 'but I do not allow photographs in the vestry. As many as you like outside church, but not inside.'

He began to bluster, 'The other Vicar used to let me take pictures of the bride and groom signing the register. What harm is there in that?'

'No harm at all,' I replied, 'but would you please leave, so that we can get the registers signed.' He still stood in the doorway. This prompted another outburst from the bride's mother.

'Why can't he take photographs of our Vera and Mick

signing the register? We was looking forward to having that in the album. After all you have done to spoil this afternoon, I think that's the least you can do.'

Remembering what my wife said about a heart attack, I took a deep breath and said quietly, 'Mrs Wilmore, I apologise for my late arrival at the church due to unforeseen circumstances, but you must understand that when I make it a rule that no photographs are taken inside church during a wedding I cannot make exceptions to it even if it were one of my own family. Now then, sir, would you mind removing yourself and your camera.'

He glared at me and left the vestry, glancing over his shoulder at me as he did so.

'Are you feeling better, Mick?' I enquired. He nodded his head. 'In that case would you please come here and sign your name in the register?' I shook his hand and then went to congratulate the bride who was still cocooned with her mother. 'Vera,' I said as I put out my hand, 'my very best wishes for a happy marriage.' I caught hold of her limp digits which were removed from my grasp immediately after contact. She did not raise her head to look at me.

The two fathers engaged in a *sotto voce* conversation in one corner of the vestry. The two mothers stood in the opposite corner on either side of the bride and groom, tight-lipped. The best man watched behind Michael John as he scrawled his name in the registers. The teenage bridesmaid examined her bouquet as if she were a keen student of botany. The atmosphere was more akin to that of a funeral than a wedding. Normally I would have preceded the happy couple and their retinue down the aisle when the vestry procedures were over. This was one occasion when I found it impossible. I opened the door of the vestry, pressed the bell button to give the organist the signal for the Mendelsshon Wedding March and stood aside as I waved them out into the nave. I could not face that congregation any more than I wished to walk with daggers in my back.

Evan Roberts came in from his seat at the organ. 'What a wedding!' he commented as he sat down on the chair at the other side of the desk. 'If you don't mind me asking, Vicar, why were you so late arriving for the service?'

'I had some business to attend to with Ivor Hodges and I hadn't realised what the time was. I shall watch that from now on, believe me.'

When I got back to the Vicarage, there was the welcome smell of liver and onions cooking as I opened the front door. My wife came from the kitchen to greet me.

'Well, did they tear you limb from limb?' she asked.

'No,' I replied. 'They froze me to death instead. Not only that, I had to contend with a bride who had blackened her face, a bridegroom who fainted and a photographer who invaded my vestry.'

'Well, my love, I am sure that none of this would have happened if you had turned up on time,' she said. 'I re-member a young curate laughing at old Canon Llewellyn forgetting to turn up for a wedding. He was found in his garage under his car and covered in grease. That young curate said that he would never be guilty of forgetting a wedding. Canon Llewellyn was in his late seventies. The Vicar of Abergelly is not yet forty.'

7

'What has happened to the bells?' enquired Tom Beynon when he came into the vestry to count the collection.

'I'm afraid all the ringers, bar Ivor Hodges, are on strike. That's why you had a solo effort this morning,' I replied. When I told him the reason for the strike, he shook my hand.

'Well done, Vicar,' he said. 'That has been a bone of contention with me for years. Why should they have the cheek to call people to worship and then walk away before it begins. The old Canon was too soft with them. There's only one thing. It will give Amos Perkins some more ammunition to get at you when he comes back from his holidays next Sunday.'

'Quite frankly, Tom, I couldn't care less about that. I am more concerned to hear about your effort to recruit volunteers for the erection of the new church. That is much more important than the Perkins tantrums.'

'In that case, Vicar, you will be pleased to know that I now have a list of twenty-two men who will be coming to the meeting tomorrow night. Jack Richards says he will be coming to talk to the men because Monday night his shop is closed. What's more he's letting his missus take over the shop in the evenings so that he will be free for the building operation. I think we can scrap the idea of a committee. He says we don't need one and, since he's going to be the boss ganger, I suppose we've got to let him have his way.'

The next evening I was in the church hall at seven o'clock

to make sure that the Scouts were off the premises before we began our meeting. As usual little Willie James, the Scoutmaster, was late arriving to supervise activities, and the boys were engaged in various forms of horseplay.

'Quiet!' I shouted in my best bel canto. There was an immediate hush. 'Now, then,' I demanded, 'how many of you are confirmed?' Seven hands went up reluctantly. I looked at the seven faces. 'Do you know what?' I said quietly. 'I have now been Vicar here for nearly two months and I don't think I have seen any one of you at the altar rails. Am I right?' There were seven bowed heads. I addressed the rest of the troop. 'How many of you are baptised?' They looked at me blankly. 'How many of you have been Christened?' All the hands went up. It was then that their leader appeared, apparently surprised at the lack of noise which had preceded his entry. He stood, blinking at me through his spectacles. 'I have been asking the members of your troop, Scoutmaster, how many of them have been to Holy Communion since I have been here and how many have been baptised. Apparently those who have been confirmed have not been to Holy Communion since I have been here and I don't know how long before that.'

'Excuse me, Vicar,' said the Scoutmaster, 'they do come once a month to the parade service at Evensong.'

'I want them at the altar rails,' I replied, 'so next month you can begin having your parade service at eleven o'clock. At least it will make certain that they have their Communion once a month. There's one other thing, before long we shall begin Confirmation classes for young people and I expect to see quite a few of those who have not been confirmed present.'

My harangue was terminated by the entry of a St John's ambulance man who was carrying a deflated rubber dummy over his left arm plus a bicycle pump in his right hand. He was a red-faced man in his forties, not much taller than Willie. This is our Vicar, Charlie,' announced the Scoutmaster. 'Vicar, this is Charlie Thomas from the Abergelly St John's Ambulance Brigade. He's going to give the Scouts instruction in First Aid. So I'm afraid we have to be indoors, but we'll be as quiet as possible.'

'I hope so,' I replied, 'because we have an important meeting in the classroom.'

By now there was a cluster of men standing in the doorway of the hall, uncertain of where they had to go for the meeting. 'This way, gentlemen,' I said and indicated the classroom where the caretaker had put out the chairs for the meeting. The next minute Jack Richards appeared in the company of Dai Elbow. They both stood, surveying the decrepit state of the hall. I went over to meet them.

'It looks to me, Vicar,' breathed Jack, 'that you need to spend as much time doing up this wreck as you do putting up the building on the estate. It can't have been touched since before the war. What a pity old Hitler didn't drop something on it then, at least you would have had compensation to build a new hall.'

'I tell you what, Vic,' added Dai Elbow, 'I've seen better pigsties than this. It will take you a lot longer to put this place right than it will to put up that church on Brynfelin. Won't it, Jack?'

The building foreman nodded his head. 'It won't help having that lot of kids let loose in here, either.'

When the time came for the meeting, all twenty-two chairs were occupied. Behind the table at the front there were two, for myself and Jack Richards. I felt it inappropriate to begin with a prayer and launched into the deep with a challenge to the volunteers to face up to the task ahead of them. Then I introduced the man who was to be in control of the operation on the new housing estate.

'Well, Vicar,' he began, 'all I can say is that I'm sorry for you. It seems to me that you've been given more than a bellyful. Before I came down here tonight I thought it was just a case of putting up a prefab on Brynfelin. After looking around this wreck of a place when I came in here, I can see you've got more than your fair share of trouble. A dozen men can see to the new church. We've got a plumber, an electrician, a painter and decorator and I've got the use of a concrete mixer from the Council. The site is flat, there's no trouble about excavating. We need a carpenter but before we can begin to do anything these walls have got to be stripped of all plaster. So anyone of you can knock plaster off a wall. You don't have to be a tradesman to do that. The sooner we get down to work, the better, believe me.'

At this stage in the meeting a large, grey-haired man with a walrus moustache, seated in the back row stood up and offered his services as a plasterer 'I'm due to retire next month,' he said, 'and I've been wondering what I was going to do to get out from under my missus' feet. So if we can get the walls stripped down in the next few weeks, I can spend all day at work. I don't know what the rest of the walls are like but I expect they will all be the same. Anyway, by the end of the summer we should have a new layer of plaster throughout.'

Jack Richards turned to me and whispered, 'I know him. He used to work for my father. 'Basket-ass', they used to call him. He's got a very big – er – bottom.'

By now the laughter and shouting from the main hall was becoming intrusive. I got up and stalked out to find little Willie Jones prostrate on the grotesque figure of the dummy, evidently intent on giving it the kiss of life. The Scouts were helpless in their mirth. I found it very difficult to avoid joining them in the general merriment.

With a supreme effort at control I managed to restrain myself and bellow, 'Can we have some quiet, please? This is the second time I have had to do this in the last hour or so.' The Scoutmaster rolled off the dummy as if he were dismounting from a stranded whale, an exercise which triggered another outburst of laughter. This time I found myself joining the Scouts in their merriment.

Willie picked himself up, adjusted his spectacles, dusted himself down and said, 'You've heard what the Vicar said. Now settle down and let's carry on with our First Aid. What was it you said, Mr Thomas, about the technique of mouth-to-mouth?'

I went back to the meeting where Jack Richards had recruited the services of Tom Beynon in compiling a list of those who were prepared to help at Brynfelin and those who would assist with the renovation of the church hall. There was a feeling of enthusiasm which compensated for the campanological disaster of the weekend. I remembered the words of my elderly predecessor on my first visit to the parish. 'If you are prepared to accept the challenge, there are quite a number of parishioners who will support you. Once the congregation see what you have in mind, you will have more support than opposition. Of that I am certain.' Emboldened by that advice from a wise old owl, I went back to the Vicarage that night more encouraged than at any other time since I had arrived at the parish.

'That must have been a good meeting!' said Eleanor when I came home. When I told her of Jack Richards' proposed two-pronged attack on the parish's building problems, she said, 'Marvellous! There's just one thing. It all depends on the amount of commitment the volunteers are prepared to give. That involves the goodwill of their wives. How long, for example, will Mrs Richards be prepared to cope with doling out fish and chips without the help of her husband?'

'Why must you always pour cold water on my plans?' I replied.

'That's better than the hot water you were in last Saturday,' she retorted. 'You must allow me to see things from a woman's point of view.' The rest of the evening was distinctly chilly.

Next morning the chill disappeared in the glow of the return of our little daughter from the hospital. We took David with us, once Eleanor's surgery was over, to escort his sister from the ward. It was touching to see the two of them hugging each other. 'David's a big boy now,' lisped Elspeth, as if they had been parted for ages. Her vocabulary was growing day by day. Marlene was most impressed by this and forecast that she was going to be very clever when she grew up. Mrs Jenkins had baked a little cake for her and had prepared a celebratory meal for us. It was a happy family occasion which I recorded with our camera.

Later that evening I had a phone call from Hugh Thomas

asking whether he could bring some of his things down to Mrs Rogers' residence before he went into retreat in preparation for his ordination on Saturday. 'By all means,' I said. 'You had better come here first, and we'll go down together. I want to see her anyway. She said she would help with the Welcome "social" we have arranged for you next Tuesday.'

'What a nice surprise, Vicar,' he replied. 'I didn't know I was to be honoured with a party to mark my arrival in the parish.'

'I'm afraid it will not be a splendid affair, Hugh. First of all, it is being held in the crumbling ruin we call the church hall and, secondly, the menu will be cakes and sandwiches, nothing more than that, washed down with cups of tea of dubious vintage. However, if the fare is not of the Ritz variety, at least the atmosphere will be much more congenial, I can assure you.'

Promptly at eleven o'clock the following day a noisy burst of engine noise heralded the approach of the elderly MG in the Vicarage drive. I went out to greet my new Curate whose open-top car was piled high with filing cabinets and cardboard boxes. 'Most impressive, I must say,' I said. 'How encouraging to see signs of a spirit of industry in my assistant and, believe me, Hugh, it's going to be essential in Abergelly.'

'I told you, Vicar,' he replied, 'when I first came to see you that I like a challenge and I meant it.'

As we unloaded the contents of the two-seater at Raglan House the landlady's eyes opened wide. 'You had better put all these things upstairs in your room, Mr Thomas. I can't have them downstairs in Mr Alabaster's waiting room.'

'That's what I intended, Mrs Rogers,' he replied. 'I wouldn't like any confidential information that may be in the filing cabinet available to his patients.'

As we carried the filing cabinet upstairs to his bedroom, I wondered what secrets were to be deposited inside it. The cardboard boxes were full of books. As we dumped them on the floor, I said to Hugh, 'It looks as if you are going to suffer from claustrophobia unless you can get some book-shelves to get these from under your feet.'

'Don't worry, Vicar,' he replied, 'I have thought about it. A friend of mine who is in our cricket team is a carpenter. I could see that there were no bookshelves in the dentist's waiting room, only ancient editions of *Tatler* and certainly nothing in my own room. So I have had a word with him and he is already in the process of making a bookstand of some oak which he had acquired. It will be ready in a few weeks, once he has stained it. I hope Mrs Rogers will have no objection to that. It is free-standing.'

'I'm sure she won't,' I said. 'She will be only too happy to have your books out of the way and on your shelves.'

As we left the house after an assurance from Mrs Rogers that she was quite prepared to have her new lodger stack his books away and that she was preparing twenty-four tuna sandwiches for the social, we returned to the Vicarage.

'In four days' time, Hugh,' I said, 'you will be coming out from that Cathedral with a clerical collar round your neck and with a feeling of exhilaration that you will be prepared to take on the whole world in the confidence that your ordination has given you. You will have been set apart by God from the rest of mankind to be His chosen messenger. The Bishop will have laid his hands upon your head and it may even come as an electric shock. Some sixteen years later, like me, you may be wondering if God has slipped up and chosen the wrong man. Hang on to that first moment of wonderment and let it support you through all the trials and tribulations which will come upon you. If you let it go, then you'll become just another moron, carrying on because there is no other job for you to do. Next Saturday I shall try to recapture the motivation which set me on the road to Damascus because, believe me, Hugh, I need it in Abergelly and so will you. Now then, would you care for a cup of coffee before you drive home?'

He rose from his chair. 'After that sermon, Vicar, which is much appreciated, by the way, I think I had better get back and reflect on what you have said.'

As his car disappeared from the drive, I wondered whether I should have been so frank in my 'sermon'. The last few weeks in the parish had shaken my faith to its foundations.

The euphoria of the meeting of volunteers on Monday night had been dampened by the comments of Eleanor, whose pragmatism had put my optimism to the test. When I contemplated the multiplicity of the problems which confronted me, I wondered whether I had the strength to cope with them. At that moment, my wife's car appeared and seconds later the key of the front door turned in the latch.

'Hallo!' she called. I came out from the study to meet her. 'What's up with you, sober sides?' she said, 'You look as if you've got the cares on your little shoulders.'

'Not so much of the little, thank you,' I replied. 'I have just been warning my new Curate of the troubles which await him once he becomes a Reverend. Two months in Abergelly have been more than enough to convince me that the "whole armour of God", as St Paul put it, will be sorely tested to cope with all that can be thrown against me.'

'Come on, love,' she said. 'It's not as bad as all that. I am sorry that I was a wet blanket last night.' She put her arms around me and kissed me. 'You are doing a great job of work with "the whole armour of God" around you, and with "the whole armour of God" around your new Curate as well, I am sure that the two of you will be able to deal with anything that Amos Perkins and company can throw at you and lots more besides. Why did the Bishop put you here? Because he knew you were the man for the job.'

After lunch, I went to the Chapter meeting at the deanery which was held that month in the church hall at St Mary's Cwmarfon. The hall was a concrete monstrosity, recently erected, evidently at the lowest possible cost. Outside it looked like a large garage. Inside, its low ceiling made it an airless prison for those unfortunates condemned to sit on its tubular chairs. It was a warm afternoon and already there was a need for an air conditioning system, which it did not possess. It was my first appearance at the clerical gathering. The rural deanery complement was considerably younger than that of my last parish, with the majority of incumbents in their forties and fifties and with a sprinkling of junior clergy.

The Vicar of Cwmarfon was an ambitious man in his late forties. He sported a goatee beard and brayed like a demented donkey. His voice was unmistakable and his chatter incessant. Tall and thin with fluttering hands, he was moving amongst the twenty or so present in an attempt to be a popular host.

'Ah!' he said as I came into the room, 'the new Vicar of Abergelly. Welcome to the deanery! I think you will find us a friendly lot. Canon Morris, your predecessor, was a great favourite here. So you have much to live up to. I'm sure you will be able to step into his shoes, as it were.'

Since my predecessor must have worn shoes several sizes larger than mine that would not be easy. As soon as he had performed his duty as mine host, he swooped upon a trio of curates and brayed with synthetic laughter at a remark one of them made to him. 'Very good,' he proclaimed and then passed on to a group of elderly clergy who were in earnest conversation. If he was after advancement in the hierarchy, at least it could be said that he was working hard to achieve it.

The next minute there was a tap on the table at the front of the rows of chairs. 'I think it is time we started the meeting,' said the Reverend Llewellyn Evans, BA, RD. 'We have a long agenda, as it were, to – er – discuss. So if you can take your places, we can perhaps settle down to – er – discuss the matters in front of us, the importantness of some of them will – er – become obvious when the time comes to – er – discuss them.'

Everybody took their places. I was sandwiched between two tall men unknown to me.

As the Rural Dean was consulting his prayer book prior to opening the meeting, the one on my right said, 'Will Evans, Llanybedw,' and shook my hand.

The one on my left said, 'Ken Williams, Aberwain,' and shook my hand.

'Gentlemen,' I replied, 'Fred Secombe, Abergelly.'

'God help you,' muttered Will Evans.

'If he doesn't,' I said, 'I'm sunk.' They both burst out laughing.

'Brethren,' chided the Rural Dean, 'let's have no more hilariousness, please, before we approach the throne of God and ask for his blessing on what we are about – er – to discuss in all seriousness, I hope.'

Then followed a long pause during which he thumbed through the pages of his dog-eared manual once again, having inadvertently closed the book to remonstrate with the unruly trio in front of him. I could feel Will Evans' shoulders shaking alongside me while Ken Williams was seized with a fit of coughing. The last time I had been in a similar situation was in my theological college when a nervous student reading the twentieth chapter of Exodus, which contains the Ten Commandments, announced, 'Thou shall not covet they neighbour's house, thou shalt not covet thy neighbour's wife, or his manservant, or his maidservant, or his axe, or his oss'. On that occasion, I was similarly sandwiched between two wags and the three of us disgraced ourselves. This time I was determined to contain myself and behave circumspectly. It was a vain endeavour.

The Rural Dean ended the pause by closing the book and saying, 'Shall we just say the Lord's Prayer together?'

I snorted, Will Evans prayed silently with tears of laughter running down his cheeks and Ken Williams suffered from a severe paroxysm of coughing. It was most uncomfortable.

The scraping of chairs as we all resumed our seats came as a great relief and with it an outburst of conversation, as the Rural Dean fiddled with some papers in front of him. The Chapter Clerk read the minutes of the last meeting.

Tobias Thomas, Vicar of Arfon, was a short, fat man, dressed immaculately in clerical grey. His business-like tones matched his appearance, that of a Company director at a board meeting. Apparently an analysis of the annual income from each parish in the deanery had shown that there had been a decline since the last analysis of a year ago. 'Coupled with the increased demands imposed by the diocesan quota upon each deanery, this presents a gloomy financial prospect.' I expected at any minute to hear of disappointed shareholders and drains upon capital funds. However, the next item in the minutes referred to a lively discussion on the subject of church youth clubs and the prospects of a deanery table tennis league. It was all so different from the deanery chapter meetings in my last parish. There the average age of the clergy was nearer seventy than sixty and the idea of a youth club table tennis league in the deanery would belong to the realms of fantasy. The only similarity was in the personality of the rural deans. Both were incapable of holding a meeting and speaking coherently.

When the minutes had been read and approved the Reverend Llewellyn Evans rose to his feet.

'My first duty is to welcome to our deanery the new Vicar of Abergelly, the Reverend Fred Secombe. Canon Joseph Morris, his predecessor, shall I say, was a member of this chapter for more than thirty years and his expertness and his deep-thinkingness was of great value to us all. I know that the new Vicar is a young man but I am sure that once he has settled down in Canon Morris' territory, as it were, his forwardlookingness and his vigorousness, from what I can gather he has shown in Pontywen, will be some compensation for the loss of, what shall I say, a priest of tremendous outgoingness and encouragingness to the members of this chapter.'

By this time I had shrunk in my chair to the size of the central character in the H. M. Bateman cartoon of the man who sneezed at a promenade concert. It was with a sense of deliverance that I heard him say, 'And now then, to our – er – agenda for today.'

The agenda for today featured a discussion on the provision of a new prayer book for the Church in Wales. Leading the discussion was the Reverend Doctor James Woodward, a beanpole of a man with a permanent frown on his desiccated features, the legacy of his dedicated scholarship. Since his doctorate was in science and was derived from a thesis on botany I wondered why he was a suitable person to pontificate on matters pertaining to worship. When I mentioned this to Will Evans later, he said, 'It's the Welsh obsession with degrees. If you are a Ph.D. then you will be considered to be a brain and, being a brain, you can pontificate on anything with the same infallibility as the Pope.'

As the Reverend Doctor droned his way through a type-written sheaf of papers, the effect of the sunshine pouring through the closed windows of the church hall induced in his listeners a drowsiness which caused a number of eyelids to close. By the time he came to the end of his treatise half an hour later there were few who were in a condition to concentrate sufficiently on what form the new prayer book should take. One or two who had come with an axe to grind, ground their way but like the mills of God they ground exceeding small. The discussion petered out eventually and the remaining items on the agenda were disposed of in no time at all, despite the efforts of the chairman to prolong the proceedings by enquiring if we were 'all of one mind'. It was obvious we were all of one mind in wanting the business to come to an end as quickly as possible.

As we stood outside the church hall in the sunshine, enjoying the fresh air after the incarceration of the previous hour or so, Will Evans said, 'I had better get a move on, otherwise I shall miss my bus.'

'If you are prepared to place your life in my hands,' I replied, 'you can have a lift with me. I shall be passing through your parish on my way back.'

'I'm quite prepared to do that, my dear Vicar. It will not only save time but money as well. As a native of Cardiganshire, the Welsh equivalent of an Aberdonian, it makes the journey doubly attractive.'

His sense of humour marked him out as a kindred spirit whose companionship would be invaluable in the years ahead.

'Joe Morris was a dear old soul,' he said, once he had settled into his seat, 'but, believe me, boyo, I can understand what a legacy he has left you. Abergelly should be the most desirable living in the deanery. Instead you have to cope with a large population to whom the church has as much attraction as I would have to Greta Garbo. For the thirty-odd years he was there, he just stood still while everything else around him expanded. Just one word of warning, Fred, don't explode in all directions at once. If you do, you will disintegrate and the parish will remain in the same state it was in before the explosion. You listen to Uncle Will.'

After I had disembarked 'Uncle Will' outside his vicarage, I returned to Abergelly in a happy state of mind. This was evident to my wife as soon as I entered the house.

'That must have been a good meeting,' she commented. 'You never came home like that from your clerical gatherings in your last parish. Don't tell me that you found your new Rural Dean an inspiration.'

'If you say silly things, my love,' I replied, 'you can expect a silly answer. He was as much an inspiration as a wet afternoon at Pontywen. The reason for the smirk is that clergy in this deanery are not in their dotage and I have found two of them with a strong sense of humour. One of them, "Uncle Will", the Reverend Will Evans the Vicar of Llanybedw, I transported to his parish on my way home. I can safely say that henceforth I can look forward to the chapter meetings if it's only to have a good giggle at the Rural Dean's mutilation of the English language. It is quite a change from the mutilation of my name by my former Rural Dean.'

'Speaking of mutilations,' said Eleanor, 'I am afraid I have to report to you that someone has thrown a brick through the east window. It has fractured St Peter's right cheek bone. Joe Williams came to report it after he had gone to clean the church this afternoon. I don't know whether you want to report this to the police or not. Joe said it has never happened before, to his knowledge. It only requires two coloured panes to heal the injury. That stained-glass firm in Cardiff could do it in no time, I'm sure.'

'Why is it that every time I feel things are going my way something happens to put a damper on it!' I exclaimed.

'Come on, Fred,' Eleanor replied. 'No one has destroyed the window. It's just a couple of panes. Most likely, it was a kid with a brick to spare.'

'On the other hand,' I said, 'it could be a grown-up with a grudge. There are plenty like that since I've arrived here.'

'Don't get paranoid, my dear,' she warned, 'otherwise you will be seeing enemies lying in wait for you everywhere. If you feel like that you had better phone the police for round-the-clock protection. Have a sense of proportion for heaven's sake!'

Her sarcasm penetrated my unnecessary concern and, by the time we were having our evening meal, my mind was at rest. It was but a brief interval of calm. No sooner had we finished dinner than the phone rang. It was Ivor Hodges at the other end.

'I have just finished doing the rounds of visiting the bell ringers, or should I say, the ex-bell ringers. The news is bad, Vicar. They are adamant that they will not come back as long as you insist that they attend church after their ringing. I have pointed out to each of them how hypocritical it was to call people to worship and then walk away from

126

the church when the worshippers were inside it. To them, campanology is a hobby and no more. So, I am afraid that, until a new team of ringers is trained, the tower will remain silent except for a solitary bell. I am prepared to do the training but I must tell you that I have many commitments and the time I can give to the task is limited. If you announce in church next Sunday that volunteers will be welcome in the tower the following Friday, we shall see what the response will be. Sorry, Vicar, it's just another headache to add to your long list since you came to Abergelly.'

I put the phone down and went into the kitchen where Eleanor was about to wash the dishes.

'The time is out of joint,' I announced; 'O cursed spite, That ever I was born to set it right!'

'OK, Hamlet,' replied my wife, 'what is it now? At least you have recovered your sense of humour.'

8

'Now then, Hamlet,' said my wife next morning as we drank our first cup of tea for the day, 'for heaven's sake don't get your knickers in a twist about the Parochial Church Council meeting this evening. I know that Amos Perkins and his band of humourless men are hoping to cut you down to size. The best way to deal with them is to keep your temper in check. Let them lose their rag, by all means. It might even be a useful ploy to invite them to do so, just to get them to make fools of themselves. I think a couple of sedatives before you make your way to the church hall won't be a bad idea. I'll bring some back from the surgery at lunch time.'

'You really are a most devious doctor,' I replied. 'I am supposed to be their father in God not an *agent provocateur* but, I must admit, there is a great deal in what you say, as usual. I'll be grateful for those tablets anyway.'

I decided to spend the morning in my study, preparing my address to the PCC. Mindful of the advice given to me by Eleanor and 'Uncle Will' of the need for a measured approach to the many problems posed by the run-down parish, I thought it advisable to drop the idea of a multiplicity of committees. It would be sufficient to let Jack Richards organise the labour for the temporary building on the Brynfelin estate and let Albert Matthews the plasterer organise the working party to renovate the church hall. That left the most important issue to be considered, the raising of the level of giving in the church collections. My predecessor used to rely on the Christmas fair to compensate for the lamentable income from the collection plate. In other words, to get the many non church goers who attended the event to subsidise the worship at the parish church. I had to find a way of shaming the congregation into giving realistically instead of insulting the Almighty by offering Him a tiny fraction of their income. It was not sufficient to make graphs indicating the average wage and the amount spent on luxuries compared with what went in a church envelope. I needed a dramatic illustration of sacrificial giving. Suddenly I remembered Emlyn Howells, my Curate at Pontywen, telling me about an instance of this which had occurred in his previous parish. It was a perfect example.

Aberllynfi was a small market town with a strong tradition of church giving. Congregations in the old parish church were large, with regular influxes of visitors who came to enjoy the splendour of the thirteenth-century church. The average giving was about a shilling a head. Then one Sunday morning the church wardens were astounded to find two pound notes inside a plain envelope. Since the collection was made with a bag and not a plate, the sidesmen who were questioned about the anonymous donor were unable to supply an answer. The Vicar thanked God for the generous visitor and assumed that such largesse was confined to that particular day. The following Sunday a similar envelope and its contents appeared once again on the table in the vestry. By now all sidesmen were instructed to take particular note of anyone putting a plain envelope into their collection bag. If the person who made this contribution was identified, then word had to be passed to one of the church wardens, who would approach the donor with a request for name and address after the service was over. When the third Sunday arrived, the source of the envelope was identified as a lady-bountiful in unpretentious dress and speaking with a Canadian accent. Since the Vicar was elderly and nervous of paying a pastoral visit to someone from overseas, Emlyn was directed to visit the address. The door was opened by an old man in a shirt and braces.

'You must be from the church,' he said, and led Emlyn into the front room where an old lady riddled with rheumatoid arthritis was seated in a wheelchair. 'My daughter's out at work and the children are all at school,' she told Emlyn.

It transpired that Joan Dixon was the widow of a Canadian ex-serviceman who had returned to his work as a coal miner after the war and had been killed in a roof fall. Joan came back to live with her mother and father who had recently moved to Aberllynfi. She had five children who were all at school and she had found work in a factory further down the Valley. In Canada she had worshipped in an Anglican church whose members had pledged to give a tenth of their income to the place of worship. She had continued this practice when she came back to this country and was still continuing to do so after Emlyn left the parish, as far as he knew. If anything was calculated to prick the conscience about the need for Christian dedication surely this was it.

While I sat congratulating myself on this memory recall, the telephone rang. It was my wife at the other end.

'There has been a very nasty accident just outside the surgery. A young man on a motor bike has been in collision with a furniture van. It looks to me as if he has a fractured skull. He has been taken to hospital. I would say that he has more need of you than he has of me. According to a by-stander, his name is Eddie Roberts and he lives on the Bryn-felin Estate at Number 30 Bevan Place. I don't think he has long to live, love, so I should get there as quickly as possible, if I were you. I hope you are not too late.'

I went upstairs to the nursery where Marlene was super-vising an artistic exercise by David and Elspeth, who were attempting to draw the Vicarage with chalk on two separate blackboards. Considering my daughter's tender age, she seemed to be more capable than her brother. I told our nurse-maid where I was going and to answer any phone calls. She asked if I knew the name of the victim. When I said 'Eddie Roberts' her face drained of colour.

'I know him,' she said. 'I've met him at the rock-and-roll dances at the Welfare Hall. He's nice but he's an awful show off. I hope he will be all right. It will be terrible if he – er . . .' She couldn't bring herself to mention death.

'I expect he will recover,' I assured her. 'Abergelly is a very good hospital with an excellent casualty department.'

When I arrived at the casualty department I was directed to the emergency ward where Eddie's bed was curtained off. From behind the curtains I could hear the urgent tones of the doctors and nurses as they tried to save the life of the badly injured youth. As I stood waiting to go to his bedside, there was an outburst of wailing in the corridor. It heralded the appearance of Eddie's mother, accompanied by a police constable who was obviously embarrassed by this unre-strained expression of grief. Mrs Roberts was a squat rosy-cheeked woman in her fifties, untidily dressed and whose hair looked as if it had not been in contact with a comb for some time. When she saw me the noise of her weeping increased by several decibels, as if my presence indicated the certainty of death and the administration of the last rites.

The Sister appeared from behind the curtain and said, 'Would you mind, Vicar, taking the lady to the waiting room outside?'

It was the cue for the constable to retire from the scene thankfully.

'I'll come back later on, Mrs Richards,' he murmured.

I led the distraught mother into the waiting room and closed the door. She refused to sit down but paced around like a caged wild animal.

'I told him that bike would be the death of 'im but, no, 'e wouldn't listen, would 'e?' she shouted. That was followed by another session of loud inarticulate howling. To try to stem this flow of emotion would be impossible, I decided. As my mother used to say of such occasions, 'It's far better out than in.' In any case, as far as I was concerned, I did not exist in her present state of mind. She was totally immersed in her desolation. I wondered how long it would be before the end would come and we would be ushered to the bedside to witness the last moments of life in her son.

The waiting room was a small anonymous place with bare walls painted in clinical white, four chairs and nothing else. It was extremely claustrophobic; I could feel my stomach churning and my heartbeats accelerating. Before long I would have to escape, whether we were called out or not.

To my intense relief there was a knock on the door and the Sister appeared. 'Mrs Roberts,' she said quietly, 'the doctor would like to have a word with you in his office before you go to see your son.' She looked at me. 'Vicar, if you would like to say a prayer with him, you can do so.'

'Oh, my God,' screeched the mother, 'don't say e's gone.'

'No, Mrs Roberts, he is still alive,' replied the Sister.

I went back to the ward where there was a nurse by the bedside of the inert Eddie. She joined me in saying the Lord's Prayer after which I prayed for his recovery and gave him a blessing.

'I can't see him recovering from that,' she whispered. 'It's a terrible fracture. Besides that, he has fractured his pelvis as well. He's in a mess, poor boy.'

As she finished speaking, his mother entered the ward with the Sister. Her hysterics had ceased by now but when she saw her unconscious son, his hand swathed in bandages, with his badly cut face, tears began to trickle down her cheeks. She made no attempt to kiss him or even touch him. Instead she looked away, as if unable to bear the sight.

'I have prayed with him, Mrs Roberts,' I said quietly. 'Perhaps you would like me to pray again now you are here.'

She shook her head. 'If you do,' she replied, 'I'll only burst out all over again. I'll just sit with him for a bit if you don't mind. Thank you all the same.'

'Is there anything I can do for you – like letting relatives know?' I asked. 'Does your husband know, for example?'

'No, its all right – I'm a widow, anyway, and Eddie's my only child.'

When I left, she was sitting by the bedside and looking at her only child by an act of will, knowing that seeing him in such a state would bring her great hurt.

I was unable to concentrate on my preparation for the

PCC meeting. The vision of the bandaged Eddie and the desolate mother dominated my mind. I kept hearing that motherly wailing echoing in the corridor. I left the study eventually and went to the kitchen where Mrs Jenkins was preparing lunch.

'I can't hear any noise from upstairs,' I said. 'I suppose Marlene has taken the children out.'

She paused in her potato peeling and brushed back a few strands of hair which had wandered over her forehead.

'They've gone across to the park, Vicar. They went soon after you came up. Marlene said that you wanted her to answer the phone while you were out. So she waited till you were back to go to the park with them.'

'I think I'll go and join them,' I replied. 'I need their company just now.'

As soon as Elspeth saw me, she came toddling across the grass to meet me. I picked her up in my arms and hugged her tight. She gave me a smacking kiss on my cheek.

'I'm daddy's girl, aren't I?' she lisped. 'You are indeed, my love.'

Memories of her in the hospital bed welled up in me and I thanked God that she was now the healthy little child in my arms. We were joined by Marlene and David who was carrying his football with him. Cricket had no appeal for him. Football was a year-round sport as far as he was concerned.

'I've saved five goals, haven't I, Marlene?' he said proudly.

She laughed. 'You're a wonderful goalkeeper, you are, aren't you? I bet you'll be at Wembley in the Cup Final one day.'

'Do you think I will be, Dad? he asked.

'If you practise every day, perhaps you will be,' I replied.

'You did kick the ball hard, didn't you, Marlene?' he

134

pleaded. 'Oh, yes, very hard,' she said. 'I always kick the ball very hard. It's a wonder I haven't burst it by now.'

'Let me have a try at kicking,' I suggested. 'I can kick very hard with my powerful left foot. You stand between those two trees and they will be the goalposts.'

'They're too wide apart, Dad,' he complained. 'I'm only little, don't forget.'

'All right, then,' I said, 'I'll take my jacket off and fold it up. Then that will be one goalpost and that tree will be the other.'

I divested myself of my garment and placed it very near the tree, leaving my son with a couple of feet to guard. In clerical shirt and bracered trousers I pretended to do a dribbling run with the ball while David stood watching at his post as goalkeeper. As I went to kick the ball, I caught my foot in a clump of grass and twisted my ankle.

'Come on, Dad, kick it,' David ordered.

I sat down and attempted to massage my ankle.

'Marlene will have to kick it,' I said. 'I have hurt my foot.'

She was holding Elspeth, both of them concerned that I was injured. All that my son felt was annoyance that he did not have a shot to save. Marlene put Elspeth down and came across to me to render assistance.

'Let me help you up, Vicar.'

She put her arm round me to help me to my feet. Once I put my weight upon my 'powerful' left foot the pain was intense.

It was a sorry spectacle which greeted Eleanor who had just returned from her morning surgery. As she closed the door of her car she was confronted with the sight of her husband being supported by her nursemaid with one arm

and the other holding a football, while the two children walked behind, hand-in-hand, like Hansel and Gretel.

'What on earth have you done to yourself?' she demanded.

'I've been playing football,' I replied, 'and I have sprained my ankle.'

'Don't tell me that David tripped you up,' she commented.

Once inside my study, I sat with the injured leg supported by a stool while my wife examined my ankle, which was considerably swollen by now.

As she probed and prodded the swelling it required a great effort of self control on my part to avoid any loud exclamation of pain. If I wished to avoid any derogatory remarks, I felt I had to prove that I was a stoic as well as a Christian.

'Well, dear Frederick,' she announced. 'You will be

pleased to know that you have broken no bones as far as I can see. However, you have a very nasty sprain which will take some days to clear up. I shall bring back a crutch from the surgery after the afternoon session. You can give a convincing Long John Silver impression if you delay your entrance to your meeting this evening. At least it will give you a sympathetic audience, apart from those, of course, who would not be moved to support you if you were carried in on a stretcher. Now then explain yourself further. How come you were attempting to score goals against your five-year-old son?'

When I explained my reason for my excursion into the football field, she kissed me. 'You are a very vulnerable soul, aren't you, my love. I rang up the hospital before I left the surgery and apparently Eddie is still clinging to life. You had better pray as fervently as you can and get your congregation to join you. It's the only hope for him. At the moment he is beyond medical care.'

I spent the rest of the afternoon and early evening reclining on the settee in the front room of the Vicarage where Elspeth and David made frequent visits to check on my condition. David wanted to talk about whether or not he would have been able to save the ball if I had managed to kick it. All Elspeth was concerned about was whether Daddy was better. What with their visits and and an excellent mixed grill supplied by Mrs Jenkins, plus glasses of red wine supplied by Eleanor, I felt sufficiently fortified to face any onslaughts at the Parochial Church Council.

It was almost seven-thirty when I made a dramatic entrance, hobbling on a crutch under my right shoulder. The reaction to my appearance was similar to that when I entered a barber's shop in Swansea during the last war, doing a Long John Silver after injuring my ankle by tripping over a pot hole. 'Hello, Padre,' said the hairdresser, 'and on what battlefield did you get that wound?'

'Oh, it's just nothing,' I replied nonchalantly.

The same look of sympathy was evident on the faces of all except the six gentlemen occupying the front six seats. One of them was Amos Perkins, who should have been occupying the empty chair alongside mine. Evidently he had come prepared for a show down, supported by his five minions. However, since that left a considerable overlap of fourteen not committed to the Amos camp, I felt that the omens were good for a successful meeting.

'What has happened, Vicar?' enquired Tom Beynon anxiously.

'I've just sprained my ankle,' I replied quietly.

Sid Thomas, the portly secretary, was puffing and blowing as he turned over the pages of the minute book nervously, apparently to give the impression of efficiency.

'Shall we all stand?' I said. They stood noisily. When silence prevailed I asked them to join in the Lord's Prayer. Another silence ensued. If the Quakers believe in the potency of saying nothing and trusting in the wind of heaven to fill their sails, why shouldn't we, I said to myself. It was a silence in which I could hear the heavy breathing of those in the chairs opposite me. I remembered the words of wisdom my wife had given me as we drank our early morning cup of tea. Now then, Secombe, I said to myself, you are about to say prayers not start a war.

'Oh, God,' I prayed, 'send thy blessing on these thy servants gathered here to wait upon thy guidance. We have much to decide under Thy divine providence for the advancement of thy Kingdom here in this parish. Give to each of us the wisdom to choose the right path and the courage to follow it to the end. Amen.'

I would have stood silent for a little longer but the strain on my ankle was causing me pain. After Sid Thomas had read the minutes, at his usual hectic pace, pausing occasionally to draw some breath for the next stint, I asked the indulgence of the meeting to allow me to remain seated for the rest of the evening. There was a murmured approval.

'Now then,' I began, 'I shan't ask if there are any matters arising, because the whole of the meeting will be concerned with them. By now you will be aware that, through the generosity of Mr Bernard Featherstone of Cardiff, we have been given a temporary building free of charge and that work will be started on its erection in a few days' time. Then there is the urgent need of the renovation of the church hall; work will begin on that next week also. Mr Jack Richards will be in charge of operations on the Brynfelin estate and Mr Albert Matthews in charge here at the hall. The response for voluntary labour has been so splendid that we can carry on both operations at the same time. I only wish that there was the same kind of response to the appeal I made for increased giving.'

At the mention of money there was a distinct chill in the atmosphere. The Amos Perkins contingent united in glaring at me while the remainder of the council looked uneasy. It was not an encouraging sight.

'There must be an element of sacrifice in our giving. Let me give you an example. In a certain parish in another rural deanery last year the churchwardens were surprised to find two pound notes in a blank envelope one Sunday morning.

They thought perhaps it was someone making a thanksgiving. The following Sunday, the envelope and its contents appeared once again.' By now my audience was intrigued. When I went on to describe the source of the giving they were most discomfited. 'A widow with five children who are all of school age,' I said. 'St Luke tells the story of the widow's mite. This example in our own diocese far outweighs that. This is why I feel we must organise a campaign to challenge our people. There is no need for a committee to oversee our building work but there is certainly a need for one to produce a plan of action which will change our conception of giving. I now throw the meeting open for a discussion on this matter.'

Amos Perkins was on his feet as quickly as a sprinter from his starting-block. Red-faced and with his finger stabbing the air in my direction, he shouted, 'Listen to him. He is supposed to be a man of God, he is more like a bank manager, only concerned about money. Canon Morris was here for more than thirty years. He never mentioned money because he felt it was his duty to look after souls not bank balances. The Vicar talks about the widow from Canada. She would have been better employed spending her money on her family. That should have been her priority. He has only been here a matter of a few months at most. In that time he has driven out one of the most devoted men in our choir. I hear he has driven out our team of bell ringers who have been in that tower for many years. Before long he will have driven out most of the congregation. We've got a Curate being ordained next Saturday – more expense. Canon Morris managed without one. I am supposed to be the Vicar's warden. He has never consulted me about any of these things. I think the time has come for us as a Council to put a stop to all these big ideas.'

He looked around as if he was expecting a round of applause from his audience. The only support he had was from his 'band of humourless men', as Eleanor described them. They were nodding their approval throughout his diatribe, like the clockwork cobbler I used to watch in the window of the shoe repairer near my home. Uncertain as to whether he should continue his peroration or not, he stood for a moment and then sat down heavily on his seat. This was the signal for 'Wot-you-Call' Williams to rise to his feet.

'I would like to second what Mr Perkins 'ave said. I've been keeping the book with the envelope numbers in them and their accounts for the last ten years.' He produced a ledger. ''Ere it is, Vicar. You can 'ave it. With an attempt at a dramatic gesture he threw the book at the table and missed. It landed on the floor in front of me. Instead of letting it lie there, he then proceeded to grovel on the floor to retrieve it and gently place it on the table. 'After all the wot-you-call that Mr Perkins was talking about, what with the new wot-you-call on the estate and the other wot-you-call by 'ere in the church 'all, I think the time 'as come for me to 'and in my wot-you-call.'

Eleanor had warned me about losing my temper. The only danger I faced was that of bursting into laughter. I caught sight of Ivor Hodges in the back row. He was wiping his eyes with his handkerchief.

I turned to Tom Beynon, who was desperately trying to keep a straight face. I felt the time had come for me to bring the farce to an end.

Despite my injured ankle, I made myself rise to deliver my *coup d'état*.

'I take it, Mr Williams, that you have handed in your resignation.' He nodded. I looked at Amos Perkins who was sitting opposite me. 'I take it, too, Mr Perkins that you wish to do the same. You have not occupied the place where the Vicar's warden normally sits and you delivered a string of insults to me. Under those circumstances I feel that you should resign as a man of honour, if you are one.'

'If I am one?' he bellowed. His face had turned from red to purple. 'Of course, I am a man of honour, even if you are not. I shall go from here now and never return. This is going to be a dark day for Abergelly,' he said addressing the Council. 'You wait and see.'

With those words he stalked out, followed by 'Wot-you-Call' Williams and the other four minions. Everybody else stayed in their seats. As the last man banged the door shut there was an evident sense of relief among the remaining members of the Council.

By the time the meeting had ended, we had agreed on a committee of three plus myself and Tom Beynon to plan a new beginning of dedicated giving in St Peter's. As we left the hall, Tom Beynon said to me, 'Well done, Vicar. Now we can start to put St Peter's on the map. It has been a joke in the Valley for long enough. As Churchill said to Roosevelt, 'Give us the tools and we shall finish the job.' We've got the men to do the building work and soon we'll have the money to back it up. Abergelly, here we come.'

'I have never seen you so animated,' remarked Eleanor when I came back to the Vicarage. 'So you kept your calm, then.'

'It was not my calm I had to keep under control but my sense of humour,' I replied.

When I told her of the events of the past hour or so, she put her arm around me and kissed me. 'I'm so happy for you, love,' she murmured. 'You deserve it. Now then, what about a spot of something to celebrate.'

We went to bed very happy and celebrated the occasion once again.

The next morning I was faced with the problem of the choice of a new Vicar's warden. Immediately I thought of Ivor Hodges, only to remind myself that the gentleman in question had already said that his appointment as keeper of the tower would mean stretching his obligations to the limit. The more I speculated about other possible vicar's wardens, the more I became convinced that Ivor Hodges was the obvious choice. Then I remembered something I had read in a church newspaper. A vicar had written in to say that 'Whenever I want anything done I always go to the busiest man in my parish'. I kept that thought in my head while I went about making arrangements for the parish visit to the ordination of the new Curate.

At five o'clock that afternoon, I telephoned the headmaster at his home and asked if I could come to see him in the evening. 'Certainly,' he replied, 'but could you make it before half past seven because I have a meeting of the Abergelly Literary Circle at the library at that time. Since I am the chairman, it is imperative that I should be there.' We agreed that I should be at his house at seven o'clock.

When I told my wife of my phone call, she said, 'Poor old Ivor! I suppose you have heard of the straw that broke the camel's back.'

'I have indeed,' I replied. 'That was quoted to me by my friend Amos Perkins some weeks ago. I had great delight in referring him to another camel quoted in the New Testament who was going to have great difficulty in getting through the eye of the needle. I think he regretted mentioning the straw on the back of his camel.'

By the time I had reached Number 13 Beaufort Crescent I was beginning to have qualms of conscience about my attempt to load another commitment on the thin shoulders of the headmaster, a much heavier one than that of the charge of the bell tower. The qualms were so daunting that I stood on the doorstep for a while, wondering whether I was doing the right thing. My mind was made up for me when the door was opened by Mrs Hodges who was on her way out, clutching her handbag.

'I didn't hear you at the door, Vicar,' she said. 'Ivor is upstairs at the moment. I'll give him a shout. Come on in, please.' She led me into the front room. 'Sit down and make yourself comfortable.' She went to the foot of the stairs and announced my presence. The next minute she was gone, explaining that she was late for a meeting of the Townswoman's Guild.

As I sat in the comfortable chintz covered armchairs in the bow window I surveyed the multiplicity of photographs in the room, from Ivor in his academic dress to his picture in his chain of office as chairman of the local Rotary Club. When he arrived in the room a little later, clad in an open-necked shirt, pullover and slacks, the uniform of a member of the 'literary circle', my discomfort grew. Why should I invade his chosen territory of favourite pursuits with a challenge which would involve a sacrifice of some of them at least?

'Well, Vicar,' he said, 'what is it this time?'

Faced with this unpropitious opening of my proposition I drew a deep breath and launched into the deep. 'In a word, or rather, in a few words, I am asking you to be my warden.'

He stared at me from his armchair opposite me. There followed a long silence, much longer than the one I had imposed upon the PCC on the previous evening. I held my gaze as I looked him in the eye. Whether it was some hypnotic power I had, as I suggested to Eleanor later, or whether it was my sheer persistence, he ended the staring session with a capitulation.

'If that's what you want, I'm your man.'

I leaped from my armchair and shook his hand frantically.

'It's not all that wonderful, Vicar,' he said. 'I'll do what I can, believe me, but there are many others who will have to pull their weight if we are to make this parish come alive.'

'Ivor,' I replied, 'it's sufficient for me if I start with you. I have to begin with the generals.'

He began to laugh. 'In that case it is just as well that you have dispensed with generals Laurel and Hardy – in other words, little "Wot-you-Call it" and Amos. After their performance last night they proved they were more fitted for the music hall than St Peter's.'

9

The next Saturday was a gloriously sunny day for Hugh Thomas' ordination. Eleanor and I were setting out for the Cathedral in her new Vauxhall Wyvern. First we stopped to say goodbye to the parishioners who were waiting outside the church hall for the arrival of their coach. Tom Beynon was looking at his watch anxiously. 'It should have been here a quarter of an hour ago,' he said.

'Go into the Vicarage,' I suggested, 'and tell Marlene that I have given you permission to use the phone to check if the coach is on its way.'

'Thanks, Vicar,' he replied. 'Some of them are champing at the bit.'

'See you at the Cathedral,' I shouted as my wife drove off.

'I hope so,' said Tom.

'So do I,' murmured Eleanor as we turned on to the road. 'The last thing you want at the moment is further discontent in the parish, believe me. Your curate's future landlady looked furious.'

'I suppose that's because she's in charge of getting people to fill the coach and to that extent feels responsible if anything goes wrong,' I replied.

When we arrived at the Cathedral there were several coaches parked outside already, with a crowd of parishioners from the various parishes involved milling around the entrance in their Sunday best.

'That means our lot will have to take the back seats,' said my wife. 'That won't go down very well.'

'It's a big building,' I replied. 'There will be plenty of room for them.'

'Ever the optimist,' she commented.

Inside the vestry there was the usual mêlée of incumbents in the process of robing, and indulging in clerical gossip while doing so. In one corner in a nervous group were the silent ordinands, awaiting their initiation into holy orders. I went across to Hugh and shook his hand. For someone who was usually loquacious, he was extremely subdued.

'All set?' I enquired.

'I hope so,' he said.

I retreated to the noisy mob at the other end. A few minutes later the hubbub ended with the entry of the bishops and the other dignitaries from the Dean's vestry. As the Dean was giving instructions about our seating, the Bishop came across to me and said quietly, 'I should like to see you after the service, Fred.'

For the rest of the morning I kept wondering why he wished to see me. At least he had said, 'Fred' and not 'Vicar'. Whatever it was, the interview was going to be friendly in any case.

As we entered the nave I looked around to see if there was any sign of the Abergelly contingent. To my intense relief, I could see Tom Beynon, Mrs Rogers and the rest, including my wife, half-way down the aisle. Then when Hugh Thomas stepped forward to read the gospel, specially chosen out of the six candidates, my cup was full. The erudite sermon by the Reverend David James Eastwood, principal of St Deniol's Theological College, passed over my head as it must have done to the laity present. I could not concentrate on his abstruse exposition, nor, I must admit, most of the service. However, throughout the laying of hands by the Bishop, I prayed hard for my new Curate and for his welfare in my parish. When the organ thundered its music as the procession moved out of the chancel, my thoughts returned to the episcopal interview and its implications. Back in the vestry, as soon as I had disrobed, I congratulated my new Curate on his ordination and on his reading of the Gospel. By now he was a different person, brimming with self-confidence and ready to face the world outside, inspired by his clerical collar which set him apart from his fellow man. I remembered feeling the same euphoria on my entry into the ministry. 'So soon passeth it away,' I said to myself in the words of Psalm 90.

'Vicar,' proclaimed Hugh, 'I have not forgotten that little sermon you preached to me in your study but, I tell you what, I feel ready to evangelise the whole population of Abergelly.' It was fortunate for him that the Bishop called me into his vestry at that moment.

He closed the door behind him and beckoned me into a chair. 'I think you should know that I have had a letter from your erstwhile warden, Amos Perkins. To say that he was not very complimentary about you would be a gross understatement. He says that you have offended many of your flock by your attitude since you have arrived in the parish and that you have acted like a bull in a china shop. Apparently you have not consulted him in any of the decisions you have taken and he felt that he had no alternative but to resign. Altogether, it is a most unpleasant letter. I thought you should know about it since he could be the source of much trouble to you outside office rather than in it. However, the picture which he paints of you is very different from the one which the people of Pontywen know and indeed the one which I know. I am not asking you to explain yourself, I am fully aware of the many problems facing you in Abergelly and I am sure you are fully capable of coping with them in your own way. You now have a Curate who should be a great help to you and if you want to use my good offices in any way please do not hesitate to do so. Now then, go and join your parishioners and your new colleague.'

He shook my hand and patted me on the back as I left the room.

'Where have you been?' demanded Eleanor when I met her at the lych gate. 'The others have all gone to the Beehive Café for a cream tea and Hugh has gone with his family to the Castle Hotel. You can take your pick. Where were you, anyway?'

'I was unavoidably detained by the Bishop,' I replied. 'He has received a letter from our mutual friend Amos Perkins. From what he told me it must have been pretty vitriolic. The great thing is that he has assured me that he feels I am fully capable of coping with Abergelly's problems in my own way and that if ever I need his "good offices", as he put it, I must not hesitate to get in touch with him.'

'The fat old . . .' She stopped in her exclamation.

'That will do, dear,' I said. 'We are still within the precinct of our mother church. It is just as well that I have an under-standing father in God. As for taking my pick, I vote that we go to the Beehive. I have already congratulated my new Curate. At the moment he is so full of his own importance that I should find him insufferable.'

'The poor little boy!' she murmured.

'Poor little boy! I tell you what, my dear Eleanor, I think that even you would find him obnoxious in his present state of mind. It will soon pass.'

'If it is as bad as that, Frederick, I hope it will,' she replied, and we made our way down to the Beehive Café, the town's biggest port of call for teetotal customers. 'I expect they will still be waiting to be served if past experience is any guide,' predicted my wife.

She was right. Despite the fact that Mrs Hughes had booked tables for forty, they were all seated by four foodless tables but in a comparatively happy mood. It was the first ordination service that any of them had attended and they were most impressed that their new Curate had been chosen to read the Gospel. They were all agreed that the only part they didn't like was the sermon. As Mrs Morrison presiding member of the Mothers' Union remarked, 'that preacher must have swallowed a dictionary'. Apparently the coach turned up at Abergelly while Tom Beynon was in the Vicarage trying to find its whereabouts. Two extra chairs were provided for Eleanor and myself and soon we were being served with cakes and sandwiches plus home made strawberry jam and an abundance of thick fresh cream. All the talk during the meal was about the welcome social for the Curate on Monday evening. Throughout this Mrs Rogers sat preening herself, mindful of her prestige as the landlady of the first curate Abergelly had been given for more than thirty years. 'I wish I was fifty years younger,' said Mrs Mabel Davies the lady who had supplied me with the information about the Earl of Duffryn. 'I think I would have been first in the queue for an introduction.'

The following morning the church was comfortably full for the parish communion service at which Hugh Thomas was due to preach his first sermon. A fair proportion of the congregation was supplied by the relatives and friends of the Reverend Hugh Thomas, who had come from further up the valley to hear him in the pulpit. When he arrived in that prominent position he brought with him a sheaf of papers which he proceeded to lay out in a flamboyant fashion on the stand in front of him. He had removed the Bible from the stand and placed it on the ledge. When the hymn before the sermon had ended he announced in theatrical tones, 'In the name of the Father and of the Son and of the Holy Ghost, Amen.' With great aplomb, he waited for his listeners to settle down. Ignoring the Bible, he announced, 'I believe in God', the opening words of the Apostles' Creed. 'Today is Trinity Sunday,' he informed his congregation. 'What do we mean by the Trinity?' Then he proceeded to expand the meaning of the 'Godhead', using terms like Monotheism, tritheism, Pelagianism, Artianism and Anthropomorphism, thrown in for good measure. By the time he had finished after half an hour, he had bewildered the natives of Aberg-elly and greatly impressed his relatives and friends who could see in him 'A Daniel come to judgement'.

As he came down from the pulpit we sang 'My God, how wonderful thou art', with his relatives gazing upon him with admiration that 'Our Hugh' could use such long words so convincingly. The normal congregation were hoping that this was not a foretaste of things to come.

When we met at Matins the following morning, Hugh's morale was high. I had asked him to read the lessons, which he did in a manner of which he thought Laurence Olivier would have been proud. I had come to the conclusion that I should bring him back to earth when we met for our Monday morning briefing. After his maiden sermon, Eleanor had been of the same opinion. 'He is a knowall supreme, isn't he?' she had said.

At nine o'clock precisely, his sports car drew up in the drive. As I looked out through the study window, I could see him leaping out of his car like one of the young bloods in a P. G. Woodhouse novel. 'The time has come, the Walrus said, to speak of many things', I said to myself. He rang the doorbell loudly as a fanfare for his entrance.

'I thought I heard the bell,' I told him. 'Come on into the study.'

Once he had settled himself comfortably into the armchair opposite my desk, with his legs crossed like a Spitfire pilot waiting for the off at an advance warning of a sortie, I launched into a blitz 'Your sermon yesterday, Hugh, was excrecable. If you preach any more like that you may as well not get up into the pulpit.' He stared at me open-mouthed. 'How dare you attempt to sum up the Godhead in half an hour of persiflage intended to impress rather than convince. Let me tell you a story about St Augustine. He was walking along a seashore contemplating the nature of God, when he saw a little boy running into the tide filling a bucket and then pouring the water into a hole he had dug in the sand. "Hallo, little boy," he said to him, "and what are you doing?" "I am trying to pour the sea into that hole," he replied. The Saint laughed. "You will never be able to contain the sea in that little hole." Whereupon the boy replied, "And neither can you, father, contain the idea of God in your little mind."

'If you are going to communicate with your congregation,' I went on, 'you must speak to them in their own language, not that of a theological text book. As from now on, you must give me your sermon by Friday morning. Then, if I think there is need of alteration, you can revise it ready for the following Sunday. I am sorry to have to speak like this, Hugh, but it's for your own good.'

He was dumbstruck, his eyes downcast as if he were examining his shoes. As I waited for his reply there was a knock on the door by Mrs Jenkins, announcing the arrival of coffee. There was a look of relief on his face like that of a boxer who had been saved by the bell. By the time he began to drink his coffee he had recovered his senses and was able to look at me.

'I'm sorry, Vicar, I know I am a bit of a show off. I should have remembered that talk you gave me when I was here last. Perhaps I was drunk with an overdose of the Holy Spirit, the same as the Apostles on the first Whit Sunday, and took it out on the congregation.'

'If I am not mistaken, Hugh,' I replied, 'I should imagine you wrote that theological treatise long before your overdose. It was to be the set piece which inaugurated your entry into the pulpit.'

Once again he dropped his eyes. Addressing his shoes, he murmured, 'Quite right, Vicar. I spent several hours over the past few weeks putting that masterpiece together.' Then, raising his eyes and looking me in the face, he said, 'Believe me. I thought it was going to be something which would put me on the map from the beginning.'

'If it is any consolation to you,' I replied, 'I, too, began my ministry on Trinity Sunday. I may not have indulged myself in the riot of pedantry which marked your effort but I can remember using the words Pelagianism and tritheism.

Perhaps it would be a good thing if the newly ordained began their ministry at Petertide, as happens in some other dioceses. Trinity Sunday is hardly the easiest time to preach your first sermon.'

As we ended our first Monday morning chapter meeting we were the best of friends. 'By the way, Vicar,' he said, 'that was a very intelligent little boy who met St Augustine on the sea shore.'

He left the Vicarage with a list of parishioners whom he had to visit during the next few days, some of whom he would be meeting at the welcome social arranged for him that evening. He had assured me that he had settled in comfortably at his new digs and had been pleased with the company of the three other residents who had joined him at the dinner table. Since they were all presentable young ladies, I was not surprised. I was sure that his fellow lodgers were equally delighted. Hugh may have been somewhat diminutive but what he lacked in height he gained in charisma, which he had in abundance. It was evident that the new Curate would be a suitable match for any aspiring female of marriageable age in the congregation. As Eleanor commented, 'They will be buzzing around him like bees in a flower bed.' At some time or another I would have to be inflicting another 'sermon' on my new assistant.

That afternoon I went to visit Eddie Roberts at the hospital. Bandaged like a mummy, he gave every indication of being one, as he lay inert on his bed. It was now some days since his accident and his condition was said to be 'stable'. There was no one at his bedside. I sat with him for some time and then said prayers for his recovery before leaving him. After that I went to the Prince of Wales ward to see

James Walters, who had been operated upon for the removal of gallstones. He was recovering very well and looked a picture of health to me. It seemed that he was due to go home next day and he was most anxious to show me the fruits of his operation which were preserved in a jar kept in his bedside cabinet.

'Here you are!' he said proudly producing his gallstones as if they were a trophy which he had won in some kind of competition.

As he did so, I was reminded of an incident in my brother's office when he was a junior clerk. One of his colleagues had undergone a similar operation and, like Mr Walters, had been given his gruesome objects to take home with him. Not content with that, he brought them to the office when he was recovered to display to fellow workers. They were passed around from hand to hand for everybody's approbation. Finally they passed to a member of the staff who was deaf and intent on perusing a balance sheet. He took the stones, popped them in his mouth and said, 'Thank you'. His horrified friends wrote a note explaining that what was in his mouth were not sweets. When they pushed the note in front of him he made a speedy exit for the lavatory, leaving the stones to decorate his balance sheet.

There was an air of excitement in the church hall as the ladies of the parish prepared the tables for the evening's big event, the first ever welcome to a newly ordained curate. There was some discussion in the kitchen about the Reverend Hugh's unintelligible sermon. A few of the helpers were of the opinion that their Curate was a highly educated specimen of the clergy who should be respected, even if they did not understand him. The rest of the ladies were con-

vinced that if he did not come down to their level they might as well go to sleep as soon as he appeared in the pulpit. However, all of them agreed that he was 'very nice' and that they would like him to come and visit them. This was obvious as soon as he came into the church hall, accompanied by Mrs Rogers, his landlady, who was carrying a cardboard box full of sandwiches and her homemade cakes. In no time at all he was surrounded by the Hugh Thomas fan club, all anxious to be introduced to him. Later when I announced that tea was ready to be served, there was a rush by the younger ladies present to join the Curate's table. 'What has he got that I haven't?' said Tom Beynon.

'At least forty years' difference and a figure minus a brewer's belly,' his wife replied.

When the refreshments were ended, light entertainment was provided by a singsong, led by Evan Roberts the organist at the piano, giving time for the helpers to clear away the tables ready for the dance which was to follow later. Next on the agenda were speeches of welcome giving me the opportunity not only to introduce the new Curate but also to announce the appointment of Ivor Hodges as the new Vicar's warden. Both wardens expressed the hope that Hugh would be happy in his first curacy, or, as Tom Beynon put it, 'take to Abergelly like a duck to water'. In reply the young man said that he already felt at home in his environment and he looked forward to working with the Vicar to make Abergelly the best parish in the Valley. This was greeted with enthusiastic applause.

The music for the dance was provided by a radiogram lent by 'Watts the Wireless' for the occasion. To the amazement of the young ladies present, their Curate demonstrated that he was expert at the new rock 'n' roll routine to the accompaniment of Bill Haley and the Comets. The two 'excuse mes' gave him no respite whatsoever. He was 'excused' so often that he must have been suffering from vertigo by the end. As I wound up the proceedings with a vote of thanks to the helpers, Tom Beynon reminded me to inform all the men present that they would either be needed on site at Brynfelin next evening or at the church hall the following evening. 'As our new Curate has said,' I proclaimed, 'let's put Abergelly on the map.'

'Well,' said Eleanor, as we drank our nightcap, 'I must say that was an unqualified success. No Amos Perkins faction to spread poison, just a warm, friendly atmosphere and a sense that a new era had begun. There was just a hint of the bombastic in your colleague's few words, but I suppose he was entitled to that. Anyway, they all loved his little speech. Now as Asquith said, let's wait and see.'

'Above all,' I said, 'let's wait and see how many turn up at Brynfelin tomorrow; that will be the acid test of the mood of the congregation. If only a handful turn up, that new era is a long way off.'

'*Nil desperandum*, Frederick,' she said.

The next morning I had a phone call from Bernard Featherstone. 'I am sorry to worry you, Vicar, but I am afraid you will have to do your own dismantling and transport of the offices at the end of next week. It seems we have a big order to take to the North of England and all our lorries will be fully occupied. I know there are a few haulage firms in your part of the world. If you can't get any satisfaction from them, give me a ring and I'll see what I can do. I think you will find that one of them will be able to oblige. You can send their bill to me. I shall wait to hear from you.'

In no time at all I was at 'Jack's Fish bar'.

'What's the matter, Vicar?' enquired the foreman builder as he led me past the range where the fat was bubbling away, ready for the first fry of the day. As we sat in the middle room, my stomach heaved at the smell.

'Trouble, Jack,' I said. 'I've just had a phone call from our benefactor to say that we have to dismantle the building in Cardiff and provide the transport to bring it here. Apparently they are too busy at the steelworks to do the job.' As I sat in the armchair by the empty grate, I must have presented a picture of complete despondency.

'For God's sake, Vicar,' said Jack Richards, 'cheer up! I know somebody who will help us out like a shot. Illtyd

158

Evans has got three "artics". His missus comes to St Peter's. They're a great family, what with him and his two sons. If you go up there now straight away, I bet you any money they will say "yes", if you ask them. Their house is on the corner of William Street and their garage is up on the hillside behind Gorse Road. I can't come with you because of the shop but you'll find the house easily. Take the second turning left from here and you'll find it at the far end of the road. By the way, I've got one or two more to come tonight, including a carpenter.'

Feeling much more heartened I drove to the end of William Street. The corner house was an imposing building – detached and with a large front lawn, bordered by a bed of standard roses. When I rang the front-door bell, I was greeted by a plump and pleasing person, as Captain Corcorm describes Buttercup in HMS *Pinafore*.'

'Vicar! How nice to you to see you.' Her face was lit with a smile which radiated friendliness. She was a lady in her fifties, with twinkling brown eyes and a neat coiffure, coloured ash blonde by a careful use of peroxide. When I sat down in an armchair in the front room, I told her the purpose of my visit.

'I am sure we can help you out, Vicar. If you don't mind, I'll go into the other room and give my husband a ring at the garage.'

There was an abundance of photographs in the room decorating the mantelpiece, the book shelves and even the window ledges. One of the photographs was that of a choirboy, a chubby youngster with a smile like his mother's. As I was inspecting her art gallery, she came bustling in.

'My husband says we'll be able to do it on Friday week.

He'll be down in a minute to have a word with you. I see you have been looking at the rogue's gallery. That photograph you have got in your hand is one of the biggest of the rogues. That's our Derek. He used to be a regular in church once upon a time, but there you are, you know what youngsters are like. He's a good boy and a great help to his father, as is his brother Malcolm there. They both drive for the firm and not only that but Malcolm's a good mechanic as well. On a Sunday they do a lot of work in the garage so I suppose I have to make up for them by coming to church myself. Would you like a cup of tea, Vicar? It won't take a second.'

When the torrent of words had ended, I realised I had not had a chance to say 'thank you'. While I waited for her to return with the refreshments, I felt a warm glow of satisfaction that someone in the parish could come to my rescue. As my predecessor had informed me on my first visit to Abergelly, 'there are plenty of parishioners who will help you once they see that you are a live-wire and are doing your best for St Peter's.' True to her word, it was not long before she reappeared with a tray adorned with a lace cloth and laden with a plate of biscuits, a pot of tea and the best china.

'I must thank you for your kindness in helping us out with your lorry,' I said. 'We would have been stuck otherwise.'

'Look, Vicar,' she replied, handing me a plate at the same time, 'if there is anything we can do to help, don't hesitate to come and ask. I know what a state the parish was in when you came. So the least we can do is to do our little bit.' As she poured out the tea, she continued with her monologue. 'I hear that Amos Perkins has resigned and that Ivor Hodges has taken his place. I tell you what, that's one of the best things that has happened since you came here. He's as mean as dirt and bossy as well. Ivor Hodges will be a good right-hand man for you. He was a great headmaster when our two boys were in school.' By this time her husband had appeared. 'I was telling the Vicar what a great headmaster Ivor Hodges was when the boys were in school.' Illtyd Evans nodded. It was obvious that he had very little else to do when his wife was in full flow. He was a thin, sallow-faced man with a ready smile like his wife. Illtyd Evans occupied the armchair opposite mine. 'Cuppa, Illtyd?' she enquired. 'I've brought a third cup, just in case.'

'Yes, please,' he replied. His voice was quiet and his manner deferential.

'Thank you very much indeed, Mr Evans,' I said, 'for coming to our aid. It's so important that we get this building up as soon as possible.'

'Well, Vicar,' he replied, 'I'm afraid I don't come to church because of the business so if I can do my bit in any other way, that's fine by me, isn't it, Annie?'

On my return to the Vicarage, I was greeted by the ringing of the telephone in the study. It was Josiah Jenkins, known to Eleanor as 'the voice of doom'. He was the upmarket undertaker in Abergelly. His sepulchral tones had been cultivated as a mark of his trade. 'Sorry to bother you at lunch time, Vicar,' he intoned, 'but I am in-between funerals. I thought perhaps you might like to see the bereaved this afternoon. It is a sudden death, you see. The name of the deceased is Winifred Louisa Thomas. She is the mother-in-law of Alderman William Owens who was Mayor last year, as you will know. I am afraid we shall have to wait until after the inquest to fix the date and time of the funeral. Mrs Owens will be grateful for your ministrations, I am sure.

They live at Caerleon House, Lime Avenue. The old lady lived with them. If you will excuse me now, I have to dash off to the next funeral.'

When I put the phone down, I tried to conjure a mental image of Josiah dashing to the next funeral. I found it impossible since his normal gait was as slow as his speech.

After lunch I went to visit the bereaved. The door was opened by a tall lady, dressed in black, her face heavily made-up and suffering from an overdose of rouge.

'Mrs Owens?' I enquired.

'Come on in, Vicar,' she said in muted tones appropriate to a house of death, 'I have been expecting you.'

Caerleon House was a three-bedroomed house in a terrace built by a speculative builder in the thirties. She led me into the front room, darkened by the drawn curtains. I sat down in an armchair facing a large photograph of herself and her husband in full Mayor array. 'Sorry to hear about your mother's death,' I murmured in a low voice, in keeping with her reduced decibels. 'Had she been ill long?'

She blew her nose. 'It was very sudden. She was a big healthy woman who loved to go shopping. She went out yesterday afternoon and dropped dead outside Marks and Spencers.' She sniffed. 'I suppose that's the way she would have chosen to go, but it's a terrible shock to those who are left behind.' She blew her nose again. 'Has Mr Jenkins told you that I would like to have her buried in that patch of grass at the back of the church? She used to be regular at one time until she quarrelled with the Vicar. I'd like a nice big headstone put up there later on.'

'Mrs Owens,' I said, 'I'm afraid you can't have a big headstone put up there. It's only a small patch of grass and in any case it is only a small casket to be buried there.'

'What do you mean 'a small casket?' she replied sharply. 'My mother was a big woman.'

'That is all that comes from the crematorium, I'm afraid,' I said.

'Well, that's it!' she said in a voice which could be heard at the end of the street. 'My mother is going to no crematorium. I'll have her buried in Abergelly cemetery. Mr Jenkins never explained that to me.'

'I take it that you would still like a service in church,' I said.

'Of course, Vicar, and all the trimmings that go with it. My mother is going to go out with dignity. I'll leave the hymns and all that to you. Now if you don't mind, I'll have to get on the phone to Mr Jenkins straight away. I'm not having my mother treated like that. A small casket indeed, and all the rest of her left behind in the crematorium. Thank you for telling me, Vicar. I would have been shocked if Mr Jenkins turned up with a little parcel in his hand. I'll let you know on the phone what time and what day the service will take place.'

As I arrived at the Vicarage, Eleanor had just pulled up in the drive. 'Why the amusement on your face, Frederick?' she asked. I told her of my interview with Mrs Owens and that lady's disbelief that her large mother could be contained in a small casket. 'I don't think it's funny,' she said. 'As far as I am concerned, if I die before you I don't want my body to be reduced to a handful of ashes. I should like to be buried in Pontywen churchyard, and not become another disposable item on the conveyor belt at the crematorium. So please remember that, my dear.'

163

'For a doctor, that seems an old-fashioned attitude to adopt,' I replied.

'Look here, Secombe,' she said tartly. 'As a doctor I respect people's bodies and care for them. At death I want my body to be respected not destroyed.'

My wife was, as always, full of surprises. We never discussed the subject again.

10

The next morning I paid my weekly visit to the bed of Eddie Roberts at the hospital. Behind the screen I found his mother seated alongside him and holding his hand. He was still unconscious but his fractured pelvis and his broken bones were on the mend. Mrs Roberts spent most of her time during the day talking to her son in the hope that perhaps he could understand what she was saying.

'I see you have started work on your little church,' she said. 'When Eddie comes out of hospital, I would like him to come with me to your services there. I used to go to church when I was a child but once I left school I left the Church as well. The only time I went to church was for my wedding and of course the cemetery chapel when my husband was buried. That was fifteen years ago. He was killed in a roof fall at the colliery. That was a terrible shock, and now Eddie. At least he is not dead. The doctor says he's got more than a fifty fifty chance of recovery. What with your prayers and mine, of course, I feel sure that one day he will be up and about.'

I said my prayers and gave him a blessing. As I left she said, 'Thank you, Vicar. I shan't ever forget what you are doing to bring Eddie back from the grave.'

She was very different from the wailing woman whose shrieks echoed around the hospital corridor on the day of the accident. Marion Richards had found a faith in God she had never known in her life, a faith she had discovered at her son's bedside.

When I came back to the Vicarage, I found 'Dai Elbow' on the doorstep. He was clad in his working outfit of jersey and tattered trousers.

'What can I do for you, Dai,' I asked.

'Can I have the key to get into the church 'all. I'm working two till ten, so I can't be there tonight. "Basket" said it would be OK for me to get cracking for an hour or so before I go to work. I've got my chisel and 'ammer in the car around the corner.'

'I thought you were in the Brynfelin working-party only,' I replied.

'So I am, Vic, but there's a lot more to be done in this wreck down by 'ere, believe me.'

I went into my study and took the keys off the hook. As I gave him the key, he said, 'There's only a few more days up there, to lay the boards ready for the concrete. All the panels are ready bolted up and then it will be left to tradesmen like me. But in the 'all it's going to be 'ard work getting the plaster off, believe me. By the way, your little Curate's a good worker, strong as an ox. He tells me 'e's going to have a trial with Abergelly. Looks a likely 'alf-back to me, Vic.'

He went down the drive, whistling the song of the dwarfs from the cartoon film about Snow White.

Marlene had taken the children to the park to enjoy the sunshine and Mrs Jenkins was preparing the lunch in the kitchen. 'A man called to see you earlier on,' she said. 'I asked him if he wanted to leave a message but he said it was private and that he would be back later.'

'He wasn't a tramp, was he?' I asked.

'Oh, no!' she replied. 'He was quite respectable.'

A few minutes and there was a ring on the doorbell. I recognised him immediately but evidently he did not recognise me. He was a middle-aged man, bespectacled and neatly dressed. 'Ah, Vicar!' he said. 'I wonder if I might have a word with you about an urgent matter. I called earlier but I was told you were out and would be back soon.'

'Come on into my study,' I replied with my tongue firmly in my cheek. I ushered him into the armchair at the side of my desk. 'Now then, what can I do for you, Mr – er . . .?'

'Williams,' he said.

'I don't know how to put this because it is somewhat embarrassing.'

'Carry on, Mr Williams,' I interjected.

'Well,' he went on, 'my one-and-only daughter lives in Sheffield and I've just had a telegram informing me that she has had an accident and is gravely ill in hospital.'

'I'm very sorry about that, Mr Williams,' I replied, 'but what has that go to do with me?'

He paused and looked at the floor. He removed his spectacles and wiped his dry eyes. 'You see, I haven't the train fare to get there. I am unemployed because of my health and living on a pittance.' He raised his now bespectacled eyes and said in plaintive tones. 'If you could lend me five pounds to pay for the fare, I would see you would have it back if I only repay you a few shillings at a time.'

'Do you know,' I asked, 'that is exactly the same amount you asked me for two years ago? Is your daughter in the same accident ward? The only thing which is different this time is that your name is Williams instead of Griffiths.

Obviously you have forgotten my face when I was in Pontywen Vicarage but I have not forgotten yours, Mr Williams Griffiths, and, by the way, your daughter was in Manchester last time.'

I have never seen anyone leap from his chair more quickly. As he moved towards the front door I called out. 'I shall be informing the police about this interview in case any of my fellow vicars suffer from your attentions.' He tried to open the door and failed. 'I suppose that I should have kept you here,' I told him. Then I opened the door and watched him walk quickly up the drive.

'I think you should phone the police and tell them about this con man,' said Eleanor when she came home from her round of visits. 'It's all very well for you because he attempted an encore. For some of your fellow clergy in this deanery it could be a premiere performance and an end to five pounds of hard-earned money. Do it now, love, before he swoops on somebody else.'

I rang the local police station and told them about the false pretences expert.

'Thank you very much, Vicar,' said the police sergeant. 'We had a call from the Reverend William Evans, Vicar of Llanybedw, earlier today. He suspected that the man was a fraud and refused to give him any money, after which he was verbally abused by him, which made him all the more suspicious. I think it would be a good idea if you would inform the Rural Dean. Then he can contact all the clergy in the area and let them know.'

When I put the phone down I told Eleanor about 'Uncle Will' and his treatment of Mr Williams/Griffiths. 'It's a pity you did not give him the same treatment when we were in

Pontywen. There you are, my dear, always the victim of the soft touch, that's you.'

'Not this time,' I replied.

'Simply because it was for the second time of asking,' she said. 'Perhaps you should go to Uncle Will for some lessons. In any case, you had better phone the Rural Dean straight away.'

'Right, boss,' I murmured as I picked up the receiver.

'Rural Dean here,' came the reply.

'Fred Secombe, Abergelly, speaking. The police have asked me to let you know that there is a confidence trickster in the district who is trying to obtain money from the clergy by false pretences. He has invented a daughter who is seriously ill in a hospital in Sheffield and he needs the train fare to get to her. The police would like you to let the deanery clergy know about him.'

There was a silence at the other end. 'Oh! Dear me! What can I say! I had a gentleman here last night. He looked to be in great desperationess and I gave him five pounds for his fare. I believed him because of his convincingness, shall I say. He said he would pay me back when he had the money. Mind you, the five pounds did not come out of my pocket, as it were. It came out of the collections we have at weddings. What you may call a fund for contingents. I could have sworn that he was as honest as the daylight. I shall tell everybody about this man, don't you worry!'

I told my wife about the Rural Dean's experience.

'Daylight robbery, of course,' she said.

'Trouble!' said Dai Elbow when he brought the church hall key back. 'I've just met Willie James after I'd locked up. He's says he've asked the Scouts to come and 'elp tonight. I told 'im that we've got enough men without 'aving that crowd of kids all over the place. "Basket" will lose 'is rag.'

'I'm sure he will,' I replied; 'so shall I, don't worry. I'll send them off to the park. By the way, do you call Albert Bevan "Basket" to his face?'

He grinned. 'No behind 'is back where 'is basket 'is. Mind, I think 'e knows 'e's called that.'

'That reminds me of an incident when I was in school,' I said. 'We had a geography master whose name was Williams but for some strange reason all the boys knew him as "Maggots". One day some unkind seniors sent a new boy with a spurious message to the classroom where he was teaching and told him to address the master as "Mr Maggots". It resulted in a clip across the ear for the innocent, and uproar in the classroom. I should think Mr Bevan would react equally as violently if he was called "Basket" to his face.'

'I bet 'e would,' replied Dai Elbow. I wondered how Dai would react if he was called 'Mr Elbow' by a similar victim of a prank.

When I went across to the church hall that evening I found a dozen or so boys in scout uniform waiting outside. 'I am sorry to disappoint you, boys,' I said, 'but I am afraid we have no need of your help. There will be a crowd of men here before long to start work. We should be getting in each other's way with too many helpers in the hall.'

As I spoke, their Scoutmaster appeared in a pair of overalls which looked several sizes too large for him.

'I have just been telling your troop that we have more than enough manpower to do the work this evening. If you had let me know earlier, Scoutmaster, I could have told you that their services would not be needed.'

He blinked at me through his thick spectacles. 'Sorry, Vicar,' he replied, 'I thought it would be a pleasant surprise for you and it would show our appreciation of the use we make of the church hall.'

'It's very kind of you,' I said. 'Now that they are here, why don't they go across to the park and make the most of what is left of this glorious sunshine?' By now a bewildered band of volunteers was arriving to be confronted by a troop of Boy Scouts. Willie James, feeling bereft of his authority by his overalls, decided to delegate his command to Douglas Owen, his senior patrol leader.

'Douglas!' he said in his deep bass voice. 'I am making you responsible for keeping order.' Then he turned to me. 'Vicar, would you mind letting me have the cricket bat and ball we keep in the cupboard outside the kitchen?'

'Not at all,' I said and opened the door. I was almost bowled over by the surge of young blood eager to be active. As they raced down towards their cupboard they discovered the debris left by Dai Elbow earlier in the day. They decided that football was more to their liking and began to kick pieces of plaster around the hall. Since Douglas was incapable of keeping order, I drowned the noise they were making with a shouted command of which any sergeant major would have been proud.

'Get out!' I shouted.

They turned tail and fled past the wide-eyed crew of plaster removers, shortly to be followed by the senior patrol leader and his emaciated cricket bat bound with black tape half-way up its length and a ball which had lost its shine some years ago.

'Don't forget to behave yourselves in the park,' ordered their Scoutmaster as they went.

'Fat chance of that,' commented Tom Beynon as he came into the hall. 'It's like asking a mad bull to behave itself in a china shop.'

Close behind him was 'Basket'. 'Thank God that lot has gone,' he said. 'Let's get down to work.'

Everybody had brought a hammer and chisel, except Willie who had only brought his overalls. When he realised that he was as unprepared as one of the foolish virgins in the parable, he decided to go home and borrow the implements from his next door neighbour. There were ten workers and the overseer divided them into pairs each with their allotted expanse of wall-to-wall strip. I had come to the conclusion that I would be unwise to offer my services since the Lord had not given me any ability to use my hands for practical purposes.

'Now then,' instructed 'Basket'. 'Work on the bottom half of the wall to start. Some of the plaster will be loose but some of it will need a lot of chipping away. Don't go knocking 'ell out of it. If you do that you will damage the bricks underneath.'

Half an hour later Willie returned accompanied by Hugh Thomas who proclaimed that he was delayed by his landlady's late provision of his evening meal. The Curate had used his persuasive powers to secure the use of tools from the monumental stone mason whose shop was at the bottom of his street. When he realised who his partner would be, he raised his eyes to heaven. After a demonstration by the foreman of what was needed, the two began their task. Soon it was evident that I would have been of more use than Willie, who appeared to be caressing the plaster with the chisel. At his side Hugh was hard at work, rapidly uncovering the bricks. By the end of the evening while everyone of the volunteers had removed a fair quota of plaster, all the Scoutmaster could show for his pains was a patch of wall decorated with what appeared to be hieroglyphics and with not a single brick to be seen.

'Next time, Willie,' said 'Basket', 'just bring a brush and you can sweep up after we have finished.'

'I second that,' said my Curate.

After Matins next morning, Hugh said, 'Would you mind if I did not come to lunch today?' It was the dentist's weekly visit to 'Raglan House' when he had to vacate his room to provide accommodation for the patients. 'My parents have invited me to join them for a special silver wedding do at the Park Hotel in Cardiff.'

'In other words Hugh, you want the day off.'

'Not at all, Vicar. I shall visit the hospital this morning and I shall be back to do some more forced labour on Brynfelin this evening.'

'My dear Hugh,' I said firmly, 'I suggest that you take the day off. A 'silver wedding do', as you put it, is a one-off occasion and I would have it on my conscience if I did not do otherwise. I shall do the hospital visiting but I am afraid I cannot deputise for you on the building site this evening. I know my limitations.'

Back in the Vicarage at breakfast, I passed on the information to Eleanor. 'That's one lamb chop less,' she said. 'Why did he not let us know about this earlier. We could have sent a card and what's more my parents could have done likewise. After all, my father and his father were college friends. His dad was evidently a late-starter in the matrimonial stakes. I

173

must say your Hugh is not as brash as I thought he would be; or you, if it comes to that.'

'I say Amen to that,' I replied. 'I did have strict reservations about him when he came to see me first and, indeed, after his ordination. However, after my first two curates at Pontywen, he is a distinct plus. Long may he continue to be so.'

She raised her cup of coffee, 'I drink to that,' she said.

When I visited the hospital I called in at the Matron's office to see if there was any patient who needed my ministrations urgently. I had established some kind of rapport with the little lady who ruled her domain with a rod of iron. She was barely five foot tall, with a face devoid of colour in which her dark brown eyes gazed intently at any newcomers, giving them the impression she could X-ray their very souls.

I was met by Mrs Darrecott, her secretary, a matronly lady with horn-rimmed spectacles, and whose ready smile offset the chilly nature of her employer. 'Matron will be back in a few minutes,' she told me.

I sat in a chair by the side of her desk and watched her typing some letters, exchanging pleasantries with her in between each stint of work. Then suddenly the door was opened and Matron swept in.

'Ah! Vicar,' she said. 'Come on in.' And led me into her inner sanctum. 'Take a seat,' she ordered. 'Somebody you know has just been rushed in suffering from a very severe heart attack. Mr Perkins the chemist. I am afraid that there is little hope of a recovery. In fact I would say that his death is imminent. I remember him telling me once that he was the churchwarden at St Peter's. So it is very fortuitous that you have turned up now.' It was one of those moments in my ministry when I felt unable to cope with the situation.

I could not look her in the face. A sense of guilt overwhelmed me. I had no doubt that I was partly to blame for his death by my antipathy towards him.

'I realise this must be a great shock to you losing your churchwarden,' she said. 'Perhaps I should not have put it so bluntly.'

I stammered a reply. 'Well, Matron, I must admit it is a great shock but – er – I am – er – afraid to say that he – er – is no longer my warden. He – er – resigned a few weeks ago. How shall I put it he – er – did not agree with the way I was running the parish. I expect that must have – er – had some effect on his condition.' I raised my eyes to meet hers, hoping for some reassurance.

'Oh, I see,' she said, with her eyes peering into mine. 'I expect it might have done but apparently his heart was in such a state that he could not have lived much longer in any case. The consultant says that it is amazing that he has lived so long.' Then she came across to me and put her hand on my shoulder. 'My dear Vicar, for heaven's sake don't get a guilt complex about this. That man could have died at any time because of his physical condition. Now then, do you want to come and see him and say prayers for him? His wife is at his bedside.'

At the mention of his wife my heart missed a few beats. She was a large lady with a florid countenance and an aggressive air. The thought of meeting her under the present circumstances made me feel like an early Christian being let loose to meet a roaring lion. I swallowed and said, 'I must go and see him. After all, he is still my parishioner, even if he's not my warden.'

She escorted me to the Thomas Griffiths ward. As we entered we were met by the Sister who was leading a distraught Mrs Perkins into her office. Evidently my prayers had to be reserved for the faithful departed and for the bereaved.

'Mrs Perkins,' announced the Matron, 'the Vicar has come to see you.'

The grief-stricken widow was transformed into a virago. 'Has he indeed?' she spat. 'Well, I don't want to see him. The further away he is from me, the better.'

I came out of the Matron's office, painfully aware that my prayers for the bereaved would have to be said at the deceased's bedside.

'May I go behind the screens, Matron?' I asked, 'to give him the last rights?'

'By all means,' she said. She instructed the nurses who were laying out the body to leave their duties until I performed mine. Amos Perkins was hidden under a sheet while I prayed that his soul would rest in peace and then besought the Lord that his widow would be comforted in her grief, something I could not give her. When I left the ward, the matron was closeted with Mrs Perkins in the office. I wondered who would take the funeral.

'So the Lord has taken away the impediment to your efforts in Abergelly,' said Eleanor at lunch.

'I don't think I would put it like that,' I replied.

'Come off it, Frederick,' she went on. 'Amos has left this world without a second of suffering. It is a kindness of the Almighty. I know it will be different for Mrs P. but, from what I can gather, she is going to be her own worst enemy. If she is going to carry a chip on her shoulder for the rest of her life, her suffering is going to be self-inflicted. Now don't go doing a repeat of the Mrs Powell episode in Pontywen. You blamed yourself for her death when you refused to accept her script for the centenary pageant. That woman could have died any moment because of the state of her heart. Now it is Amos Perkins. He was grossly overweight, obviously suffering from high blood pressure and now, from what you tell me, had a heart which was disintegrating. Get things into proportion, Vicar. You have done everything according to your conscience. If everybody did that in life, the world would be far better off, believe me.'

'It's not as simple as that, my love,' I said. 'Why are there wars in the world? It's because each side's conscience is clear that they are in the right.'

'Look, Secombe,' she replied, 'if you want to indulge in a bout of self-flagellation, that's up to you. You will not do yourself any favours if you do. You will suffer and so will your parish.'

A little later that afternoon Tom Beynon appeared on the doorstep. 'Have you heard about Amos Perkins?' he asked.

'I think you had better come in, Tom,' I said. Once we were seated in my study I told him of my visit to the hospital and the reaction of Mrs Perkins.

'I'm not surprised about that one little bit, Vicar. She can be very nasty and this will make her a real problem in the parish. She will go around telling everybody that it's your fault that he died. There's only one way to fight that kind of talk. You've got to make it plain that he was a sick man. Make a start by writing a long piece in next month's magazine. You can say that he was a pillar of St Peter's for many years but that no one suspected that he had a bad heart and could have dropped dead at any time. The congregation are getting to know you quite well by now and they will judge things not by what Annie Perkins says but by the kind of man you are.'

'Thank you, Tom,' I replied. 'I shall do that. There's just one outcome of all this that bothers me. He should have his burial service conducted in this church but I can't see her agreeing to that if I am to take the service.'

'I wouldn't be surprised if she asks Canon Morris to come back for the funeral,' he said.

'I hadn't thought of that,' I answered. 'I could be absent unavoidably and she would not have to see me.'

'How about a dose of flu?' he suggested.

The more I thought about it, I became convinced that my predecessor should be the man to preside over the obsequies of his former churchwarden. 'I don't know about the dose of flu, Tom, but I am sure you are right about Canon Morris. I shall ring him after you have gone. Thank you very much for your help.'

As soon as he had left, I rang the Canon. 'I was just about to call you,' he said. 'It has all been a bit embarrassing. Annie Perkins has asked me to take Amos' funeral. First of all, it was a terrible shock to learn that he had died and secondly it was just as much of a shock to find that he had resigned his post as warden. I have no wish to enter into what brought about his resignation. I could imagine that he would be a stick in the mud. All I can say is that I am quite prepared to take the service if you want me to do so.'

'I should be most grateful, Canon,' I replied, 'if you would take the funeral. Apparently she thinks I am responsible for his death and has no desire to see me. I must respect her wishes and I shall not be present. If you will let me know what hymns she requires, I shall let the organist know.'

'I am so sorry about this, Vicar,' he said. 'I told you that there would be the diehards in the parish who would oppose any change you wanted to make. Evidently Amos led the opposition, from what Annie tells me. Don't lose heart, my boy, you do whatever you feel the parish needs. I tell you one thing. The Bishop made the right move when he appointed you.'

That evening I went early to the hilltop site. A large rectangle of crudely dug soil had been excavated from the waste patch of ground, ready for the building of what Mrs Roberts had called my little church. Down below, I could see St Peter's church with its square tower standing out as a landmark. Once upon a time, I said to myself, there had been a similar rectangle cut out of the valley to accommodate that impressive stone building. My thoughts went to the Earl of Duffryn whose forbears had paid for its construction. I wondered whether my visit to him in a few weeks' time would ensure that the 'prefab' we were about to erect would be replaced by a permanent church which would dominate the hilltop as effectively as its mother church below. My musings were ended by the noisy appearance of Stan Richards' Ford van.

'You're here early, Vicar,' he commented.

'I felt I needed some fresh air.' I replied, 'and where better to get it than up here.'

'Quite right,' he said. 'By the way, I expect you've heard that Amos Perkins has died.'

I wondered what he would say further and nodded my head. 'Well, from what they tell me, he was more of a hindrance than a help in St Peter's. Mind, it must have been a great shock to his missus, but what a way to go. I always tell my missus that, when I die, I'd like to die with my boots on. So he was a lucky man, wasn't he?'

'He was indeed,' I replied. By now the pioneer corps was arriving with their implements, filled with enthusiasm for their voluntary work. I remembered what Eleanor had warned me about self-flagellation that morning. 'With support like this,' I told myself, 'and the endorsement from my predecessor, just keep right on to the end of the road, Secombe.

11

By the following Tuesday the eve of my visit to James Davenport Herbert, Earl of Duffryn, the base for the new church
had been laid. The volunteer squad had levelled the concrete
expertly under the watchful eye of Stan Richards and surrounded by spectators from the estate where interest in the
construction of the buildings was beginning to grow. At least
when I met the Earl I could tell him that the temporary place
of worship would soon be in place. Hugh Thomas had been
a tower of strength and had gained the respect of all the men
who were involved in the operations both on the hilltop and
down in the church hall. His enthusiasm was infectious and
an encouragement to his fellow workers. At last I had a
young Curate, strong in mind and body, who helped rather
than hindered. So I had no hesitation in asking him to assist
Canon Morris at the funeral of Amos Perkins that afternoon. It was at the Canon's suggestion that I did this. He
thought that the presence of one of the parish clergy would
be an adequate mark of respect, coupled with the attendance of both the churchwardens and members of the Parochial Church Council. To my surprise, my wife decided that
she would go to the service.

'I could not stand the man,' she said, 'but I shall be there
to represent you since you have been banned from your own
church. I shall give you a full report when I return.'

At two o'clock Ivor Hodges began to toll the big bell in

the church tower. My Curate came into the Vicarage to see if I had any last-minute instructions to give him. 'Do you want me to give out the hymn numbers?' he asked. 'What about the psalm? Is that going to be said or sung?'

'Look, Hugh,' I said to him. 'Since Canon Morris is taking the service, you ask him those questions. As far as I am concerned, it would be wiser to say the psalm since there is no choir.'

A quarter of an hour later Eleanor came into the study and kissed me. 'It's not very often that I have the privilege of representing you,' she told me, 'but here I go. As you can see, I am wearing my gaudiest suit. To wear black would be very hypocritical of me. I could never say I could mourn his passing. See you soon.'

As she went out, I was aware of my guilt complex returning. Here I was, a prisoner in my own Vicarage, while next door in the parish church a former Vicar's warden of ten years' standing was to be given the funeral rites with his Vicar conspicuously absent. Perhaps I could have reasoned with him more instead of indulging in confrontation. I went into the sitting room, opened the top of the radiogram and began to play the records of the D'Oyly Carte performance of *The Pirates of Penzance*, which the Pontywen Church Gilbert and Sullivan Society had given as their present on our departure. 'Here's good luck to Frederick's ventures,' sang the pirates in the opening chorus.

'Not much luck, so far,' I said to myself. 'Perhaps tomorrow will bring a sea change in the tide of fortune.'

I picked up the letter from the Earl which I had left on the occasional table earlier that day. I had read it several times already, trying to find out signs of encouragement, without success. There was not an atom of commitment, apart from the acknowledgement that 'his forbears' had built the parish church many years ago. I read it over once again and came to the conclusion that it would need a tidal wave of good fortune to produce anything worthwhile from the noble gentleman. I put down the letter and proceeded to walk about the house like a caged animal. The children had gone out with Marlene. It was Mrs Jenkins' day off. The D'Oyly Carte company sang without an audience. When the first record ended, I called a halt to their performance and went out into the garden.

I could hear the strains of 'Abide with me' coming from the church. I looked at my watch. It was five to three. Evidently the service was coming to its close. Soon I would be out of my misery with the arrival of my wife and my Curate. Five minutes later Eleanor walked up the drive.

'I escaped from the back of the church before the cortège got under way,' she said. 'It's a good thing you weren't there, love. There was a scratch choir composed of Herbert Evans, the yawning king, "Wot-you-Call" Williams and four other buddies of the late Amos. I could not believe my eyes when they appeared.'

'I don't doubt that,' I exclaimed. 'What a cheek! Where was Hugh Thomas when they came into the vestry? What about Evan Roberts, if it comes to that?'

'I expect he was in his seat at the organ, and I don't think young Hugh could have thrown them out anyway. In fact the Curate read the lesson very well indeed. Apart from giving out the hymn numbers, that was his only contribution to the service. The Canon paid a brief tribute to the deceased, said the prayers and led the cortège in and out. There was quite a crowd there. The Rotary Club, the Bowls Club and people like that. Not many parishioners, though. Well, that's over now, my dear. The Lord has removed your biggest headache. So just calm down and relax. You have a long journey in front of you tomorrow and you will need to be at peace with yourself if you want to make a good impression on his nibs.'

A little later the Curate arrived, looking sheepish. 'I'm sorry, Vicar,' he said. 'Dr Secombe must have told you about the unauthorised choir. Half a dozen men came into the vestry, claiming to be ex-choristers. One of them, an aggressive bloke with glasses, said he had been in the choir since a boy. So that was it. They all knew the Canon quite well and he had a word with each of them. It was only after the service that the wardens told me who they were, the refugees from the Parochial Church Council. One of them, who kept saying, "wot-you-call" every other second, had a dreadful voice, loud and off-key.'

By now, I had simmered down. 'That, my dear Hugh, was the famous "Wot-you-Call" Williams, aide-de-camp to Amos. As far as I know, I don't think he was ever in the choir. Don't worry, there is nothing you could have done about it. According to my wife, you read the lesson very well. That is what matters. You did not let the side down.'

'Thank you very much,' he replied with manifest relief. 'I shall always do my best, I can assure you of that. When the wardens put me wise to the invaders of the vestry I was very much aware that I had put my foot in it. After my first sermon, that is something I did not want to repeat. By the way, the Canon told me that he would be getting in touch with you this evening to let you know how everything went. He is quite a character, isn't he? He said that the Bishop must have thought that you have asbestos fingers by giving you a hot potato like Abergelly to cope with. Then he went on to say, "Mind, some of the heat has gone out of the potato today." "What an irreverent Canon!" I replied, but how perceptive. On the other hand why did he heat up the potato in the first place.'

That evening, as we enjoyed our cod and chips from 'Stan's Fish Bar', Eleanor said, 'I feel sure that this is a milestone in our stay in Abergelly.'

'That's a quick milestone,' I replied. 'We have only been here a matter of months.'

'You know perfectly well what I mean, Secombe,' she retorted. 'If you are going to do all that is needed in this parish, and that is a big "all", the one essential above everything else is the parish behind you one hundred per cent. With the demise of the only person who could orchestrate any opposition, I see no reason why, from now on, you should not be able to look to the future without having to worry about what is going on behind your back.' She raised her glass of cheap white wine from Jones the off-licence round the corner from the Vicarage. 'Here's good luck to Frederick's venture,' she proclaimed. 'Hold on,' I said, 'how did you come to say that? What a coincidence! I happened to be listening to *Pirates*, when you were in church.'

'I knew that,' she replied. 'I noticed that the lid of the radiogram was still aloft. I could see that you had been listening to our parting present from Pontywen. Wouldn't it be nice if we could start a G & S Society in Abergelly.'

'You must be joking,' I said. 'With all that we have in the way of commitments it would be like contemplating climbing Mount Everest.'

'What does the Bible say about faith moving mountains?' she enquired.

'That's moving them not climbing them,' I said. 'In any case whether it is moving them or climbing them, by the time we are ready to think about a G & S Society we shall be far too old to take part and we shall have to leave it to our children who will be grown up by then.'

'It's just a dream,' she replied.

At nine o'clock I received a phone call from Canon Joseph Morris. 'My apologies for ringing you so late, Vicar,' he said. 'My wife and I were invited back to the Ivor Hodges residence for some hospitality which turned out to be a three-course meal. Ivor has been telling me about your trials and tribulations and about how well you are coping with them. I am so sorry to have left you such a mess to clear up. I wish I had known about your contretemps with Herbert Evans. It would have been a pleasure to suggest to him that he and his crew should leave the vestry. He was a thorn in my side for many years. I would like to have been present to see you ordering him out of his seat in the choir. Anyway, the service this afternoon went without a hitch. Your young Curate read One Corinthians fifteen beautifully. Thank you for allowing me to take the service. God bless you.' With that he put the phone down.

'Who was that?' asked Eleanor.

'Just my predecessor apologising for the fact that we can't start a G & S Society.'

I spent a sleepless night. My mind was far too active to allow me any repose. Not only was I speculating on the various possible outcomes of my interview with the Earl but

I was faced with the prospect of a long journey in my Ford 8 down to South Devon. I had written to the noble lord informing him that I would be there by two-thirty p.m. This would give me enough time to cope with any emergencies on the way, I thought. There was the obstacle of the Aust ferry across the River Severn to be faced. The one and only time I encountered it was on our honeymoon drive to Newquay. On that occasion I had almost landed our car in the river. Eleanor took charge on the return journey. There would be no Eleanor tomorrow.

At six o'clock next morning I was ready to begin my fateful expedition. Mrs Jenkins had prepared me a pack of sandwiches. I had marked out my route in the road map of South West England I had purchased earlier. My RAC card was in my wallet. My cheque book was in my inside pocket. Wearing my first bespoke clerical grey suit, which my wife had insisted that I needed to make an impression at Somerton Castle, I took my seat at the steering wheel in the vehicle which had been serviced the previous day at Evan Morgan's garage. I wound down the window and my wife kissed me.

'Drive carefully,' she instructed. 'You have loads of time. Don't worry about the ferry. Just watch the signal from the ferryman and you will be OK. You have a lovely day for the trip. So just sit back and enjoy it.' She kissed me once more and I made my way down the drive.

The traffic was very light. Newport was half asleep as I passed through it and in no time at all I was driving down the lane which led to the ferry. To my dismay there was a long queue of cars waiting to be transported. It seemed an eternity before I became next in line to drive up the ramp. I had wound down the window to be prepared for the shouted instructions. Gingerly I began to embark upon what seemed an unnecessarily narrow means of boarding this Noah's Ark. An irate ferryman indicated that I should stop. He came down the ramp to me.

'Didn't you watch my signals!' he shouted. 'Now then, wait until I have gone back up. Then right hand down until I tell you to straighten up.'

Sweat had stuck my new Wippell's clerical shirt to my body. I waited until he had gone back to his place and then revved up the engine as if I was about to get prime position in a Grand Prix. He gave an impression of Toscanini frantically indicating to an over zealous orchestra that he wanted more diminuendo. I obeyed immediately and then stalled the engine. He shook his head in disbelief. Impatient drivers behind me began to make their presence felt by pressing on their horns. I decided that an arrow prayer was the only answer. After I had closed my eyes for a brief moment, I opened them and slowly moved up the ramp on to the ferry.

'Well done, Vicar,' said my guide sarcastically. 'Perhaps you will do better on the other side.' I did.

Once I had reached the A38, after some difficulties in Bristol, I felt in complete control of the situation. The traffic was quite heavy by now but I was making my way steadily, and with hours to spare. My Ford 8 was incapable of burning up the miles, but it allowed its driver to enjoy the countryside as he made his way leisurely to his destination. There was a bottleneck at Taunton but, once I was clear of that, I felt that before long I would not be far from the Earl's residence. I had another four hours before my appointment with my potential benefactor.

Then it happened. A few miles north of Collompton. Suddenly the car veered off the road and down into a ditch, a deep ditch. My face came into contact with the steering wheel. It was a painful meeting which robbed me of my senses for a moment. With an aching jaw I managed to extricate myself from the car and climbed on to the roadside. Cars passed by me, oblivious of my signals to stop. I felt like the victim ignored in the parable of the Good Samaritan. Then he stopped and came to me. He was a lorry driver with a cattle truck full of bleating sheep en route to the port of Newhaven. He did not bind up my wounds or take me to an inn but he drove me to the nearest call box.

'I think you should call for an ambulance as well as the RAC,' he said. 'You should have that face seen to.'

'It's all right,' I mumbled through my aching mouth. 'I've got to be at Little Trentham in Devon by half past two for an important appointment.'

'Well, Vicar,' he replied, 'I think you should have an appointment at the hospital before you go there.'

I rang the RAC and they promised they would have someone there 'as soon as possible'.

As I came out of the call box the pain in my jaw became intense. I sat by the roadside, with my face cupped in my hands, trying to assuage the acute discomfort. To my great relief, an RAC van pulled up outside the call box.

'Hello, Vicar!' said the serviceman. 'Big trouble, is it?'

'Big trouble, indeed,' I replied, 'both to my car and to me. I have a very important meeting with the Earl of Duffryn in a few hours' time and my Ford 8 is in a ditch a few miles further back outside Collompton.'

'By the look of you, you need attention as well as your car,' he said.

Minutes later we were both surveying the crash. He went down into the ditch. 'Tyre burst,' he pronounced. 'We'll have to get a crane from Taunton. It will only take minutes to replace the wheel. I take it that you have a spare in good condition.'

'I have indeed,' I said. 'It was only serviced yesterday. How long will all this take?'

'With a bit of luck,' he replied, 'we should have the crane from Taunton in less than an hour. So you should be away fairly quickly after that. What time is your appointment with the Earl?'

'Two-thirty,' I told him.

'I suggest that you phone him and tell him that you may be delayed. Your face looks in a bit of a mess to me. Would you like me to take you to the hospital in Taunton, for a check-up?' he enquired.

'Not on your life,' I said. 'If I am going to hospital it will be after I have seen the Earl, not before.'

'As you please, Vicar,' he replied.

We sat together in his van, with the midday sun burning the metal and turning the vehicle into an oven, despite the opened windows.

'Have a drop of orangeade,' he invited and poured it into the plastic cup which covered the flask. It was then that I realised how badly my jaw had been affected. To open my mouth sufficiently to admit the liquid into my mouth gave me excruciating pain. I prayed hard that the crane would arrive as quickly as possible. Half an hour later the rescue squad arrived and in no time at all the slightly tattered car was back on the road. Soon the spare was in place and I drove off towards Little Trentham, asking St Christopher where he had been earlier and praying that he would be at my shoulder for the rest of the day. Evidently he heard my prayer and I arrived at Little Trentham by two o'clock. It was a delightful village built apparently in Elizabethan times and untouched by human hand ever since. A rivulet trickled down through the middle of the village green, as it had done from time immemorial. It was the kind of place where the clock had not moved for centuries.

I sat on a bench and tried to compose myself for the meeting with the Earl. Thought was difficult. The pain in my face was too dominant. At twenty past two I went across to my car, which was disfigured by a bent bumper and a liberal coating of mud over the bonnet. Once inside, I looked at myself in the driving mirror. It was not a pretty sight. My face was bruised and swollen. This was not how I had imagined I would present myself at Somerton Castle. I had passed the imposing entrance, with its lodge and wrought-iron gates, on my way down to the village. The gates were open as my Ford 8 crawled up the drive through the immaculately kept parkland. After a few minutes, I turned a corner and there facing me a few hundred yards away was a masterpiece of turreted building, fronted by rolling lawns on either side of the drive. A coat of arms decorated the wall above the arched main doorway. To complete the picture of opulence, a Rolls Royce gleamed in the afternoon sunshine outside the door. I parked my mass-produced vehicle a discreet distance away from it to avoid any immediate comparison.

With my stomach churning I braced myself to meet the possessor of all this wealth. Before I could press the button inset on the stone pillar, a voice said, 'Hello, Vicar.' I turned round to see a tall, grey-haired man informally dressed in an

open-necked shirt, pullover and baggy trousers. 'I saw your car on its way when I was in the paddock.' He shook my hand firmly. He had a pleasant smile and put me at ease instantly. 'Come on in.'

I had decided to give him one 'sir' when I met him and to leave it there. However, he was so disarming that I did not bestow even that upon him. He led me into his study, whose walls were lined with enough books to have stocked the public library at Abergelly. A massive leather-topped desk was the principal piece of furniture with a number of expensive-looking leather upholstered chairs scattered around the room. He ushered me into one of these and brought another alongside it.

'Now, before we talk, would you care for some refreshment? You have had a long journey.' He went across to a drinks cabinet amply supplied with decanters and glasses. 'I should like a large tot of whisky, please,' I mumbled. 'I am afraid I had an accident on my way here and I think I have injured my jaw. As you can see from my speech, it is an effort to open my mouth. However, I am sure I can open it enough to imbibe some scotch.'

He turned his attention from the cabinet and looked at me, moving towards me to conduct a closer investigation. 'My dear fellow,' he said, peering at my face, 'you certainly are in a bad way. Perhaps you should go to our cottage hospital for a check up. I had better not pour you a large one, as you suggest. We don't want any more accidents, do we?' He went back to his private bar and dispensed a modicum of whisky for me and a generous helping for himself. As I accepted the cut glass tumbler from him, I found it difficult to murmur my thanks.

'If you don't mind,' I went on, 'perhaps we could cut our *tête-à-tête* short. You see, my wife is a doctor and the sooner I get back to her the better. I think I should leave the check up until then.'

It was indeed a short *tête-à-tête*. The Earl had my letter on his desk and had decided what he would do some time ago apparently.

'Well, Vicar.' he said, 'it seems that you have ten years of worship in your homemade tabernacle in front of you before it has to be dismantled. That is a fair amount of time to raise money for your permanent church. Quite obviously you are a young man of energy and enthusiasm. I propose to give you an equal amount of money to whatever money you raise. When my forefathers paid for the building of your parish church, they were the only source of money for its erection. This is 1954. You minister in a mining valley where everyone is in full employment, thank God. I am sure that between us we shall be able to see a permanent place of worship on the Brynfelin estate. As a betting man I would say that's an odds on chance.'

This news acted as a most effective analgesic. By the time I had said goodbye to my benefactor and had driven out of his estate I was more conscious of euphoria than I was of the discomfort of an aching face. It seemed no time before I was confronted with the second crossing of the River Severn. At half-past seven in the evening there was no long queue on the English side. A different ferryman was in charge. I was determined to board the vessel without incident. Grimly I bent over the steering wheel, holding it so tight that my knuckles stood out white on my hand. At the signal to move up the ramp, my nerve failed me. I was stranded. The driver of the car behind me came out and enquired what was wrong.

'I'm afraid I just can't drive up there. I had an accident earlier today and my nerve has gone,' I explained ignominiously.

'Get out, Vicar,' he ordered. 'I'll take your car on the boat. You get in the passenger seat of my car.' Seconds later the Ford 8 was aboard the ferry and my rescuer came down the ramp to join me in his car. 'Don't worry,' he said, 'I'll do the same for you the other side.' I thanked St Christopher for providing me with a clerical collar. Were it not for that item of clothing, I doubted that I would have had such cooperation. Eleanor always referred to it as 'slipped halo'.

She was at the Vicarage door before I could get out of the car. 'What on earth have you been doing with your limousine?' she enquired when I opened the door to greet her. 'More importantly, my dear love, what have you been doing to your face?' she said.

'Never mind about that,' I replied, 'it's worked. He's going to give half of the cost of the new church.'

'I don't care what he is going to give,' she said vehemently, 'you have got a nasty injury to your jaw. In fact it looks as if you have dislocated it. Come in and let me have a closer inspection and then it is off to the hospital for you.'

I got as far as the Vicarage porch and then passed out. The next thing I knew was that I was laid out on the couch in the sitting room. 'Stay still,' my wife ordered. 'If you can open your mouth enough to take this, we'll have you up at the hospital for an x-ray.'

With a potent painkiller in me, I was whisked off to Abergelly hospital by my wife. My jaw was photographed, and in no time at all I was anaesthetised in the operating theatre. When I awoke the sun was streaking through the window of the little side ward and Eleanor was sitting beside me.

'Well, Marco Polo,' she said, 'how do you feel?'

'Give me a chance,' I replied with considerably less difficulty than at my last attempt to speak.

'That sounds much more intelligible than your Esperanto last night,' she commented. 'When you are more comfortable, jaw wise, you can give me a full account of your perilous journey. From what I can gather you have achieved your objective, my little hero. All I can say is that you must have endured a hell of a lot of pain on your way back. I don't know how far you drove in that condition but you deserve a medal.' She kissed me gently on my forehead. 'That's enough kissing for the time being,' she added.

The next day I was back home at the Vicarage, eager to get out and about in the parish. I had been visited by my wardens and my Curate at the hospital. In a few sentences I had informed them of my success in Devon. Joy was unconfined. A new dawn was breaking, they said. It was Eleanor who advised against the rose-coloured spectacles. 'You have to raise many thousands of pounds, love. It will not be easy. It's one thing to make a brave one-day trip to Devon. I am proud of what you did but now there is a hard slog of ten years' sweat, toil and tears ahead of you. It could be much more wearing on you physically than a dislocated jaw, believe me.'

I rang the Bishop that evening to let him know what the Earl of Duffryn had promised.

'My dear Fred,' he said, 'I am so glad to hear it. As you know, the diocesan funds are not exactly overflowing at the moment. Perhaps in a few years' time we shall be able to make a contribution. I think it would be a good idea if you contacted the local press and gave them the news. The more publicity you get in your campaign to put the church on the map in Abergelly the better. It is good for the community to be made aware that St Peter's is alive and kicking once more.'

Encouraged by this episcopal support, I contacted the *Monmouthshire Gazette* who said they would send someone to the Vicarage. The someone was a cub reporter not long out of school, by his appearance. As we sat in my study drinking coffee he wanted a full account of my mission to Devon. When he heard of my accident and my dislocated jaw he spent more time writing about that in laborious longhand than he did recording the generosity of the parish's benefactor. As a result, when the newspaper appeared in print later that week, I was the feature of a long article on the front page under the heading, 'VICAR'S NIGHTMARE JOURNEY'. The Earl of Duffryn was accorded a single sentence at the end, indicating that he had promised to give financial backing for the building of the new church.

Reading the purple prose of the aspiring journalist, Eleanor said, 'So much for the Bishop's suggestion that the community should be made aware of the Earl's generosity. I doubt if anybody noticed the final sentence.'

'Well, any publicity is better than none,' I replied.

'That, Frederick,' she retorted, 'is an over-used piece of garbage.'

12

'Steady with that panel, boys. If you drop it, you'll break the glass in the windows.' Stan Richards was overseeing the unloading of the redundant offices from the 'artic'. One of that particular volunteer gang was Willie James who had deserted the church hall plaster strippers because of his demotion to sweeper-up. His appearance on the Brynfelin scene was greeted with as much enthusiasm as the arrival of a teetotaller at a stag party. Inevitably it was his side of the panel which showed signs of hitting the ground. Dai Elbow rushed to the rescue. 'For God's sake, Willie, get out of the way,' he ordered. He grabbed hold of the panel and pushed the Scoutmaster aside with such force that he came into facial contact with the wet grass, an experience shared by many of Dai's opposing forwards.

It was the Friday evening of the deadline for the removal of the prefabricated building from the steelworks. Six men had gone down with the lorry to help with its dismantling. Now at seven o'clock, in one of those drizzles which afflict the valleys, they had arrived with their precious cargo. Waiting outside were a dozen more volunteers, excited at the prospect of erecting the church the next day when everybody would be off work and ready for action. By the end of the evening, the labourers were drenched but happy that all was ready for D-Day. The weather forecast was promising and hopes were high. As I got out of my car at the Vicarage, Ivor

Hodges' recruits were ringing an uncertain finale to their practice in the bell tower. His new team included three young ladies, one of whom was Marlene. She was the most enthusiastic member but the least competent, according to Ivor. 'She's on the treble bell where she can do least harm,' he had told me. 'Still, in time I am sure that she will be more accomplished. Marlene is a big girl, as you know. Once she knows the ropes, if you will pardon the pun, she might be able to ring our big tenor bell.'

'I shall look forward to that,' I said.

When I came through the front door I was singing lustily a snatch from the trio in *Iolanthe*: 'Nothing ventured, nothing win, blood is thick and water's thin.' Before I could get any further, my wife came out from the sitting room.

'We've had enough noise from the bells this evening without you adding to the cacophony. In any case, why this unrestrained vocal exercise?' I caught hold of her and hugged her. 'Frederick, you are wet and you have been drinking,' she exclaimed.

'Nothing of the sort, my dear,' I replied. 'I am wet, yes, the same as all the other slave labourers, but, drunk, no. Let's say I am intoxicated with the sheer delight of seeing everything come into place. Tomorrow a church will arise on the Brynfelin estate and now when I return home I am greeted with a salute from eight bells, rung by churchgoers instead of pigeon fanciers.'

'I would hardly call it a salute,' she said. 'Unless you mean it resembles the unholy noise of the firing of cannons on the Queen's birthday. Before you indulge in any more euphoria, I have to inform you that you have had a phone call from "Wot-you-Call" Williams. He wishes to come and see you, as far as I could make out from the plethora of "Wot-you-Calls". I have told him to ring you at nine o'clock tomorrow.'

'What on earth can he want?' I replied with a grimace.

'I thought that would wipe the smile off your face,' said my wife.

Promptly at nine o'clock next morning the phone rang. 'What can I do for you, Mr Williams?' I asked.

'Well I'd like to come and see you about a wot-you-call for Amos Perkins. As you know, he was wot-you-call for fifteen years. That's a long wot-you-call of time, isn't it? Mrs Perkins won't come to see you because of all the wot-you-call. So she has asked me to do the wot-you-call.'

'Well, Mr Williams,' I said. 'I am afraid I shall not be able to see you today. At ten o'clock we are all meeting on the Brynfelin estate to put up the new church and I shall be there all day. How about next Monday evening at, say, seven o'clock? Will that suit you?'

'Thank you, Vicar. That will be fine. I'll bring all the wot-you-call with me,' he replied. His tone was conciliatory, far different from his attitude at our last encounter.

'Beware of the ravaging wolf in sheep's clothing,' warned my wife when I gave an account of our conversation. 'Especially if Annie Perkins is behind this.'

'Let's wait and see,' I said. 'In the meanwhile I have more important things to do today than to speculate about the nature of "Wot-you-Call's" visit.'

At a quarter to ten Hugh Thomas turned up at the Vicarage to join me for our great day. The weather forecast was accurate for once, and yesterday's drizzle had given place to a gloriously sunny morning. I had decided to wear an open-necked shirt under a somewhat moth-eaten pullover and a pair of old trousers which I used for my occasional forage into the garden. My Curate arrived in his rugby shirt and shorts.

When he appeared on my doorstep, he said, 'This is a whole different ball game! Do you mind travelling in my vintage MG, Vicar?'

For a vintage car it was remarkably speedy, coaxed by the young man at the driving wheel. In no time at all we were approaching the building site on which the big eight foot by eight foot panels had been stacked neatly the night before. To my dismay as we turned the corner to enter the street which overlooked it, there was no sign of the stack. Instead there was a bunch of men examining the chaos of scattered sections of our new church. I was out of the car before Hugh had switched off the ignition.

'What on earth has happened?' I said to Jack Richards who was surveying the scene, his face purple with indignation.

'Bloody yobbos!' he exclaimed. 'Look at the broken windows and the dents in the panels where they have been using their hobnailed boots.' He pointed at the three in front of him. 'Some of the others are worse than these.'

'Perhaps we should have fenced off the site,' I said.

'A lot of bloody good that would do,' he replied and then apologised for his language. 'Sorry, Vicar, but it makes your blood boil when you see something like this. I suppose we were lucky that they didn't mess up the concrete. As far as fencing it off is concerned that would be no protection. Not even a ten-foot-high wall would stop them.'

'Does that mean we can't put up the building?' I asked.

'Oh, no!' he said. 'We'll go ahead and then we'll have to

repair it once it's up. "Basket" will be able to see to the plaster board inside. The panels are very strong. They'll have to put some roof felting on the outside. What is important is that we have to get it up before they can do any more damage.'

At this stage in the proceedings Dai Elbow appeared. 'If I could catch the buggers who did this,' he shouted, addressing the street, 'I'd break every bloody bone in their bodies.'

'Steady on, Dai,' I said. 'This is a church we are building not a boxing ring.'

'Sorry, Vic,' he replied. 'It's very 'ard to be Christian when you see something like this. There's only one language these – er – blighters will understand and that's a fist in their faces, I can tell you.'

By now there was a full complement of volunteers reporting for work. Jack called all of them together for a 'pep' talk.

'Look, lads,' he began, 'I know you must all be disappointed, to say the least, at what has happened. There's only one way to show those who did it that they haven't won the day and that is to put up this church right away. You all know your own particular gang. I'll tell you what panels you each have to put up. I take it that those who have to bolt them together here brought their spanners, etcetera with them. So let's go, boys, and show them that nothing they can do will stop us building this church.'

Soon the desolation was giving place to an ordered process of construction. Although I had changed into some old clothes for the occasion, I decided not to impede the efforts of others by attempting to help with my hands.

Instead, I occupied my time by exhortation. I was joined in this by Willie James whose oversized overalls were once again rendered superfluous as each gang assured him that they had no need of his assistance.

'I know I am not a person of great stature,' he said to me, 'but I have very strong hands. They don't seem to realise this.'

'Have you brought your car?' I asked him. He nodded. 'Well, I think the best thing you can do is go down into the town and bring back some bottles of beer from the off-licence. It's going to get very warm before long and the men are going to be very thirsty.' I gave him two pound notes and, to the intense relief of his fellow volunteers, he disappeared from the hive of activity. By one o'clock a third of the building was in place. Most of the windows were broken but the felt exterior was undamaged because the panels were face downwards. There were some minor marks on the interior, that was all. When Jack Richards called a halt to the proceedings for the lunch break, the workers were in good heart. Willie James had added another pound note to the two I gave him and came back with enough crates of beer to keep everybody happy for the rest of the day.

As the workers sat down and ate their packs of sandwiches, washed down by the local brew, the two church wardens arrived on the scene. Tom Beynon had been working six till two, while Ivor Hodges had been watching his school cricket team play an important match. The headmaster had arranged to pick up his fellow warden and both came clad in overalls, ready to relieve anyone who needed a rest from their labours.

'I don't believe it!' exclaimed Tom when he saw the broken windows.

'I do.' replied Ivor. 'I have a large intake from the estate in my school and quite a few of them are a real headache, I can tell you. I would suggest, Vicar, that you put wireguards around the glass as an immediate priority. Otherwise you will be spending a small fortune at the glass merchant's.'

'Well, Vicar,' said Tom, 'you told me that what brought you to Abergelly was the challenge it would give you. It looks as if Brynfelin is going to be the biggest challenge of all. In that case, it's up to us to do everything we can to help.'

'Thanks, Tom,' I replied. 'The first way will be to do a house-to-house visitation to let the people know that we have arrived on the hill and that we want to do all we can to care for them in this God forsaken place. They must feel that they are a human rubbish dump. There are no shops, no post office. Until my wife started her practice, no doctor. We must use this building not only as a place of worship but as a centre for the community where young and old can meet in all kinds of organisations which will cater for their needs – youth clubs, young wives' clubs, old-age pensioners' clubs, that sort of thing. If you treat people as though they are second class citizens, they will behave like that.'

At this stage in our conversation, I felt a tap on my shoulder. I turned round to see a large lady dressed in a sack-like garment which went down as far as her ankles, where it met a pair of sandals enclosing a pair of feet which had not seen water for some considerable time, it would appear.

'Excuse me,' she said, 'but can you tell me what's going on by 'ere.'

'We are building a new church,' I replied.

'It's a funny sort of church,' she went on, 'more like a pre-fab than anything. Mind, it's about time that something was done up 'ere, even if it's only a church. I 'eard a lot of noise last night and opened the bedroom window and saw a gang of yobbos pushing that pile of building stuff all over the place. I told 'em I was going to call the police and they went off.'

'Thank you very much,' I said. 'By the way, it's going to be more than a church. We'll have a youth club, a mother's meeting and all that sort of thing. It will be for everybody, not just a few.'

'Great!' she replied. 'Just the kind of thing we need. I expect it's that new Vicar. E's 'Arry Secombe's brother, isn't 'e?'

Tom Beynon interjected. 'This is the Vicar.'

'Well!' she said. ''E doesn't look a bit like 'im, does 'e? Thin as a rake compared with 'is brother.' She turned to me. 'Pleased to meet you, Vicar. I'm sure my two boys will want to come to your youth club. It'll keep 'em off the streets, won't it?' Then she waddled away quickly, evidently to tell her neighbours that she had met 'Arry's brother.

As she went, Ivor said to me, 'If her two boys are coming to your club you had better keep an eye on them. They are holy terrors. I recognised her immediately. She has come storming to the school to complain about her innocents receiving corporal punishment. Her name is Spolanski, married to a Polish escapee who joined the Air Force at the beginning of the war. It's a good thing I was disguised in these overalls. Our last encounter was not exactly harmonious. She has a fine turn of phrase when she is roused, I can tell you.'

'Forewarned is forearmed,' I replied. 'At least they will not have corporal punishment in our youth club.'

It was not until seven o'clock that the final stage of construction was completed, the placing of the roof on the four walls. Some of the men had gone home by now. The faithful remnant raised a cheer as Jack Richards and 'Dai Elbow' placed the panel in position. They came down the step ladder in a state of exhaustion.

'I said we'd finish in a day,' proclaimed the foreman, 'and we've done it.'

'Aye,' replied 'Dai Elbow', 'and it's bloody well done us. Sorry, Vicar.'

'Don't apologise, Dai,' I said. 'Quite frankly I don't know how you have managed to do so much in such a short space of time. Jack, you have been an inspiration. Without you, there would have been no church on this site.'

'Thank you, Vicar,' he replied, wiping the sweat from his brow, 'but there's still an awful lot to be done inside. This is just the shell. Dai, here, will have to do all the wiring. Henry Evans has got to do the plumbing. Arnold Templeman to do the painting. "Basket" will have to do his job. This is just the start. I've done my bit and now they've got to do theirs.'

'And what's more,' I added, 'I have to do my bit. There's all the church furniture to see to. I am afraid it will have to be second hand, as far as I can see. From the altar to the seating accommodation, it is going to be a policy of begging from other parishes or it may be from other chapels. In any case, I am determined to have everything by the time our experts have made their construction. It won't be before long that we shall have the Bishop here to consecrate the building.'

When I arrived at the Vicarage, I was met by Eleanor. 'You look all-in, love,' she commented and kissed me. 'Before you tell me what has happened on Brynfelin, I have some news you will be very pleased to hear. I have had a phone call from the hospital. Sister Thomas on Eddie Roberts' ward rang to say that he has recovered consciousness at last and that it seems his brain is not damaged.' I began to weep. 'Frederick,' she said, 'you are supposed to be the rock on which your faithful place their trust and confidence.' I stifled any further show of emotion.

'All right, love,' I replied, 'I am supposed to be a caring rock. Don't forget that there was an occasion when Jesus wept over someone. In fact these are tears of happiness. The church at Brynfelin is now erected. Those men have been heroes. It has been a hot and sultry day, as you know, but they have slaved as if their lives depended on it. My dear love, I feel that God will be with us in all that we do in Abergelly. If I may put it in a banal way, the news about Eddie Roberts is the icing on the cake.'

I slept the sleep of the just that night and awoke to find the rain belting on the window panes. When I opened the curtains, lightning flashes stabbed across the leaden sky.

'Secombe,' called my wife behind me, 'you are a lucky devil.'

'Last night,' I replied, 'I told you that I felt God is with us. That is nothing to do with luck or the devil. If this had happened yesterday, there would have been no church on Brynfelin.'

'Have it your own way,' she said. 'What about a cup of tea to start this miserable day? In any case, I'm only pulling your leg, as you well know. If I started getting pious, I don't think you would like that.'

'I certainly wouldn't,' I murmured. 'Would you like me to get back in bed?'

'For the time being,' she said, 'I would prefer a cup of tea, if you don't mind. In any case, since this is the day of the week when you work, I think you will need all your strength to cope with that. But you can give me a cuddle before you start brewing up.'

I gave her a cuddle which took a quarter of an hour.

Despite the weather there was an unusually large congregation at the family communion service. All the volunteer force was present. Some of them with their wives and families. A rather unexpected influx to the worshippers was the trio of young ladies from Hugh Thomas' lodgings. As he ascended the pulpit for his peroration, I surmised that he must have told them that he was to be the star billing that morning. Since he had been heavily involved in all the physical work in the parish that week, I told him that he need not bring his written sermon for my approval. His three admirers formed a fan club in the pew directly behind the choir seats, gazing up at him in rapt adoration. When he read out his text which had nothing to do with the collect, epistle and gospel, I felt that he was about to launch into a Hugh homemade homily.

'St Luke, Chapter five, verse thirty-eight,' he announced; 'but new wine must be put into new bottles.' Ignoring the script he had placed on the stand in the pulpit, he looked around at his listeners before he began to speak. 'Yesterday I was privileged to be present at a new birth, one which concerns every one of you present at this service. Before the Vicar and I left for the Brynfelin estate, there was nothing there other than a pile of panels ready for building. When we arrived that carefully stacked pile of building material had become strewn about the place in a chaos of broken glass. Nine hours later a church had arisen with a battered exterior, but a church. You in Abergelly have been given a challenge by the induction of a new parish priest. He is a new bottle into which God has poured new wine.' By now his voice was raised. 'The former things have passed away. They signified stagnation, smugness, blindness to all that was going on around. From now on we must all face up to our responsibilities.' He went on to talk about Paul's journey to Damascus, giving a detailed account of the saint's background and emphasising the drastic change brought about by his conversion. 'Now that light has shone suddenly on the road from Abergelly to Brynfelin and I pray that your eyes have been opened by the new battle which has brought the new wine of spiritual regeneration to the people of this parish.' He then quoted the text of his sermon once more with great emphasis, having ignored it for at least three quarters of his address. His audience was enthralled by the passionate nature of his oratory and were oblivious to the mixed metaphors involved. Indeed, had it been possible, they would have given him a standing ovation for his effort. There was no doubt that the Reverend Hugh Thomas was going to make his mark in the parish amongst young and old.

As we stood at the church door, shaking hands with members of the congregation, compliments were showered upon him.

At lunch Eleanor spoke of his eloquence. 'I hope you will add your contribution to the chorus of praise for Hugh when you meet for your weekly conflab tomorrow. It's the first time you have had such a devoted statement of support from one of your curates. Your first two assistants were stumbling blocks to your ministry and your last one was not with you long enough to be of much use.'

'If he had stuck to his script,' I replied, 'perhaps he would not have mixed up the bottle of wine with the light on the road to Damascus. His sermon made it sound as if the light Paul saw on his journey was due to the bottle.'

'Oh, come off it, Secombe,' she retorted. 'You know perfectly well that you are exaggerating the extent of his mixed metaphors. That sermon was spoken from the heart, just as yours are. I hope the green eye of jealousy has not begun to affect your vision as far as Hugh Thomas is concerned. I am afraid you don't realise how well blessed you are to have someone like him. You don't preach a written sermon. Why should he?'

That point was incontrovertible. It is true that my first Vicar never asked to see my written address. I could have preached off-the-cuff from my first appearance in the pulpit as far as he was concerned. That is why I never bothered to write out my sermons after I found I could get away with a couple of notes which I had jotted down because I had spent the Saturday in frivolous pursuits.

'Ah, well, we shall see,' I said. 'In any case I am seeing Hugh on Tuesday. He is taking a funeral at ten o'clock tomorrow. One of the pauper's burials from what used to be called the "Workhouse". Not only that, but I am looking forward to visiting Eddie Roberts tomorrow morning. I am wondering how he will look with his eyes open and if he will be able to speak to me.'

The Curate and I met for matins at nine o'clock next morning. I studiously avoided any mention of his sermon and gave him some addresses I wished him to visit that afternoon. It was apparent that he expected me to say something about his *tour de force*. He left the vestry with his head bowed, disappointed that he had received no accolade. As he shut the door behind him I felt a pang of remorse. I realised that if I had been in his shoes I would have felt the same.

An hour later I had forgotten the episode in my excitement at the prospect of seeing Eddie out of his coma. When I entered the ward, I went into the sister's office where I was greeted with a rare smile from the normally stern-faced lady.

'Well,' she said, 'he has pulled through and as far as we can see with no brain damage. He says very little but he is coherent. I think he is awake. His mother is with him, inevitably. She has been tremendous, speaking to him every day in the hope that he could hear her. She is one of the reasons why he has regained consciousness, I think. Anyway, you go and see for yourself. The screens are still around his bed but we shall be removing them once Dr Llewellyn has been to examine him.'

I made my way to his bed with my heart pounding. Gingerly I moved one of the screens to make an entrance. Before I could get to the young man's bedside, Mrs Roberts came up to me and held my hand. 'Isn't it wonderful, Vicar? I'm sure your prayers have helped a lot.' She turned away from me and addressed her son. 'Eddie, this is the Vicar who has been praying for you here and in church.' I looked at the young man. His eyes were open. They smiled at me and so did his mouth which had been drawn to one side by his accident.

'Hello, Vicar,' he managed to say. 'Thank you.'

They were four words which will always remain in my memory. Soon afterwards he fell asleep. I thanked God for his recovery and gave him a blessing. As I left the mother and son, I felt that this was the most important moment in my ministry since I had come to Abergelly. A prefab on Brynfelin and a restored church hall came second.

That evening at seven o'clock the door bell at the Vicarage announced the presence of 'Wot-you-Call' Williams. The little man appeared on my doorstep nervously clutching an unfurled umbrella which he had brought more for support than protection from the rain, since the sky was unclouded.

'Come on in, Mr Williams; leave your umbrella in the rack. He manoeuvred his umbrella into the receptacle after two attempts and then followed me into my study. My visitor was so ill at ease that I felt sorry for him. When he sat in the chair opposite me, he began to twiddle with his thumbs.

'Now then,' I said, 'what kind of memorial to Mr Perkins do his widow and his friends envisage.'

He stared at me. 'All we want is a small wot-you-call somewhere in wot-you-call part of the church up by the altar. You know the kind of thing: 'In memory of Amos Perkins who was wot-you-call of the church for fifteen years.'

'In other words, Mr Williams, you are proposing a plaque in the chancel. I am afraid that such a memorial is not allowed nowadays. The only kind of memorial would be a stained-glass window or something of that sort. I can assure you that the advisory body appointed by the Church would not permit a plaque to be placed on the wall. Otherwise there would be plaques all over the place for various parishioners. Perhaps you might suggest to Mrs Perkins the idea of a stained-glass window in the nave of the church. There are at least three windows where that might be done.'

Quite obviously the cost of a stained-glass window compared with that of one piece of stone or slate was giving the late Churchwarden's henchman great concern. His face was a picture of misery. He had to face Annie Perkins with a financial outlay of considerable proportions to which he could not contribute in any significant way. 'Wot-you-Call' Williams attempted to copy his departed ring leader by an unconvincing foray into the realms of bluster. 'I think this is dreadful. 'Ere is a man who 'as given 'is life to serving 'is church and that is all the wot-you-call they can give in return. I think it's wot-you-call. Let me tell you this, I shall be writing to the Monmouthshire wot-you-call about this, you wait and see.' He stood up in a show of indignation and proceeded to the front door.

'Hold on, Mr Williams,' I said 'don't forget your umbrella.'

I waited as he tried to extricate it. After his third unsuccessful effort to retrieve his unfurled means of support, whose spokes were in conflict with the rack, I closed them together and then lifted the umbrella out of its stranglehold. I opened the door for him.

'Would you kindly tell Mrs Perkins that the rules have not been laid down by me, but by the Church?' I added. He grabbed the offending article and made his way out with not a single 'wot-you-call' left to utter.

No sooner had I closed the door than Eleanor came out from the sitting room to enquire what had transpired in my encounter with my visitor.

'Typical,' she said. 'What that plaque should have told its readers is "This is a man who always wanted something for nothing and who died without giving anything to his church".'

'Hold on,' I replied. 'That's going a bit too far.'

'Not far enough in my estimation,' my wife said, 'when you think of all this parish needed and for fifteen years he did nothing to help it.'

'That was not his fault,' I told her. 'That was down to Canon Joseph Morris.'

'I hope you remember that when you speak with your Curate tomorrow,' she retorted. 'You have someone who is prepared to give his all to help you in your fight to resurrect the Church in Abergelly.'

At matins next morning, I prayed for the parish and all its needs. I prayed so earnestly that Hugh Thomas and I knelt in silence for minutes afterwards.

As we came into the vestry, I said to him, 'I have had more headaches in the first few months I have been in this parish than I had in all the years I was in Pontywen.'

He nodded. 'I can appreciate that, Vicar, in the few weeks that I have been here.'

'By the way,' I replied, 'thank you for your sermon last Sunday. It's good to have such support from the pulpit. We both have been led into pastures new and the shepherding will have to be a joint responsibility.' I put my arm around his shoulders. 'I may be the senior partner, but don't forget that you, too, are a partner.'

'That's very kind of you, boss, to promote your junior so early in his apprenticeship. I'll do my best to live up to it,' he said and his face was split by a wide grin. Then he added, 'Let's hope the waters of comfort flow more freely from now on in the pastures new.'